总 策 划：许　琳

总 监 制：马箭飞　王君校

监　　制：张彤辉　王锦红　韩　晖

主　　编：吴中伟

编　　者：吴中伟　高顺全　吴金利　吴叔平

改　　编：吴中伟

顾　　问：陶黎铭　陈光磊

翻　　译：Christina P. Chen　Catharine Y. Chen

译文审订：Jerry Schmidt

Contemporary Chinese

For Beginners

Dāngdài Zhōngwén

当代中文

吴中伟 主编

Liànxí Cè
练习册
Exercise Book

华语教学出版社
SINOLINGUA

First Edition 2010
Fourth Printing 2014

ISBN 978-7-80200-691-1
Copyright 2010 by Confucius Institute Headquarters(Hanban)
Published by Sinolingua Co., Ltd
24 Baiwanzhuang Road, Beijing 100037, China
Tel: (86)10-68320585 68997826
Fax: (86)10-68997826 68326333
http://www.sinolingua.com.cn
E-mail: hyjx@sinolingua.com.cn
Facebook: www.facebook.com/sinolingua
Printed by Beijing Jinghua Hucais Printing Co., Ltd.

Printed in the People's Republic of China

Mùlù 目录

Contents

Dì-líng Kè　　Yǔyīn
第0课　语音
Lesson 0　Phonetics

0.1

Listen and repeat

ā á ǎ à	ō ó ǒ ò	ē é ě è	
ā ǎ	ē ě	ō ǒ	
á à	é è	ó ò	
ā à	ē è	ō ò	

bā	bá	bǎ	bà	pā	pá	pǎ	pà
bān	bán	bǎn	bàn	pāo	páo	pǎo	pào
bāi	bái	bǎi	bài	pāng	páng	pǎng	pàng
dē	dé	dě	dè	tē	té	tě	tè
fēi	féi	fěi	fèi	mēn	mén	měn	mèn
jiāo	jiáo	jiǎo	jiào	qiān	qián	qiǎn	qiàn
huō	huó	huǒ	huò	suān	suán	suǎn	suàn
zhōng	zhóng	zhǒng	zhòng	chōng	chóng	chǒng	chòng
lū	lú	lǔ	lù				

0.2

I. Sound discrimination

1. Indicate which one you hear.

(1)　A.　pō　　　　　　B.　bō　　　　　[　　]

(2)　A.　dē　　　　　　B.　tē　　　　　[　　]

(3)　A.　ó　　　　　　B.　é　　　　　[　　]

(4)　A.　bō　　　　　　B.　dé　　　　　[　　]

(5)　A.　yí　　　　　　B.　yú　　　　　[　　]

(6)　A.　lì　　　　　　B.　lù　　　　　[　　]

(7)　A.　yǔ　　　　　　B.　wǔ　　　　　[　　]

(8)　A.　mō　　　　　　B.　mó　　　　　[　　]

当代中文

(9)　A.　nà　　　　　B.　ná　　　　　[　　]
(10)　A.　bǐ　　　　　B.　bí　　　　　[　　]
(11)　A.　tā　　　　　B.　tà　　　　　[　　]
(12)　A.　pì　　　　　B.　pí　　　　　[　　]

2. Fill in the blanks with the initials you hear.

(1) _____à　　　(2) _____à　　　(3) _____ō　　　(4) _____ō
(5) _____ǎ　　　(6) _____ā　　　(7) _____ǔ　　　(8) _____ú
(9) _____á　　　(10) _____ā　　　(11) _____ì　　　(12) _____ǐ
(13) _____ē　　　(14) _____ē　　　(15) _____ó

3. Fill in the blanks with the finals you hear.

(1) m _____　　　(2) m _____　　　(3) n _____　　　(4) n _____
(5) l _____　　　(6) l _____　　　(7) f _____　　　(8) f _____
(9) t _____　　　(10) t _____

4. Mark the tones you hear.

(1) ta　(2) ta　(3) ta　(4) ta　(5) da　(6) da　(7) da　(8) da
(9) yi　(10) yi　(11) bi　(12) bi　(13) wu　(14) wu　(15) di　(16) di
(17) yu　(18) yu　(19) ma　(20) ma　(21) na　(22) na

5. Listen and write down the syllables you hear.

(1) _____　　(2) _____　　(3) _____
(4) _____　　(5) _____　　(6) _____
(7) _____　　(8) _____　　(9) _____

II. Listen and repeat

ā	á	ǎ	à
ō	ó	ǒ	ò
ē	é	ě	è
yī	yí	yǐ	yì
wū	wú	wǔ	wù
yū	yú	yǔ	yù
bō	bó	pǒ	pó
bǔ	bù	pǔ	pù
mō	mò	fō	fó

dā	dà	tē	tè
dī	dì	tī	tí
nǔ	nǚ	lù	lǜ

III. Listen and repeat

é	goose	è	hungry
wǔ	five	wù	fog
pá	climb	pà	be afraid of
bà	father	bā	eight
dǎ	strike, hit	dà	big
tā	he, she, it	tǎ	pagoda
mā	mother	mǎ	horse
ná	take, carry	nà	that
bǐ	than	pí	skin, leather
mǐ	rice	nǐ	you
nǚ	woman	lǜ	green
lù	road	bù	no, not

IV. Listen and repeat

yúfū	fisher	fùyù	rich		
dìyī	the first	dìyù	hell	tǐyù	sports
dà yǔ	heavy rain	dà yú	big fish		
dàyī	overcoat	dàyì	careless		
yílǜ	without exception	yìlì	willpower	lìyì	benefit
dìtú	map	túdì	apprentice	tǔdì	land
fǎlǜ	law	fǎlì	supernatural power		
lǐ fà	have one's hair cut	lìfǎ	legislate		
pífū	skin	bǐyù	metaphor		

0.3

I. Sound discrimination

1. Indicate which one you hear.

(1) A. gǔ   B. kǔ   [   ]

当代中文

(2)	A.	gān	B.	gēn	[	]
(3)	A.	kǎo	B.	kǒu	[	]
(4)	A.	dǎi	B.	děi	[	]
(5)	A.	tán	B.	táng	[	]
(6)	A.	lóng	B.	léng	[	]
(7)	A.	kǎo	B.	kào	[	]
(8)	A.	gān	B.	gàn	[	]
(9)	A.	hǎo	B.	hào	[	]
(10)	A.	máng	B.	màng	[	]
(11)	A.	tāi	B.	tài	[	]
(12)	A.	dǒng	B.	dòng	[	]

2. Fill in the blanks with the initials you hear.

(1) _____ āi　　(2) _____ āi　　(3) _____ ǎo　　(4) _____ ǎo

(5) _____ ěn　　(6) _____ ēn　　(7) _____ áng　　(8) _____ áng

3. Fill in the blanks with the finals you hear.

(1) b _____　　(2) b _____　　(3) p _____　　(4) p _____

(5) m _____　　(6) m _____　　(7) t _____　　(8) t _____

(9) t _____　　(10) k _____　　(11) k _____　　(12) k _____

(13) k _____　　(14) k _____　　(15) h _____　　(16) h _____

(17) h _____　　(18) h _____

4. Mark the tones you hear.

(1) gao　　(2) gao　　(3) gao　　(4) gao　　(5) kafei

(6) bangmang　　(7) gaokao　　(8) kanwu　　(9) laodong　　(10) tengtong

(11) nenggou　　(12) fennu　　(13) daode　　(14) paodan　　(15) dafeng

(16) tanlan　　(17) botao　　(18) hanleng

5. Listen and write down the syllables you hear.

(1) _____　　(2) _____　　(3) _____

(4) _____　　(5) _____　　(6) _____

(7) _____　　(8) _____　　(9) _____

6. Listen and mark the syllables you hear in the neutral tone.

(1) gege　　(2) keyi　　(3) boli　　(4) dangan　　(5) yikao　　(6) yifu　　(7) houlong

II. Listen and repeat

āi	ēi	āo	ōu
ān	ēn	āng	ēng
bái	bèi	bàn	bāng
páo	pǒu	pén	pēng
mài	méi	fēi	fǒu
dàn	dāng	tóu	tòng
nǎi	néng	lǎo	lóng
gǔ	kǔ	hǔ	

第 0 课

III. Listen and repeat

bàba	father		māma	mother
nǎinai	grandma		gēge	elder brother
mèimei	younger sister		tāmen	they
nǐ de	your		dòufu	tofu
nǎodai	head			

IV. Listen and repeat

ài	love	ǎi	(of height) short			
gàn	do	gān	dry	gǎn	dare	
gǒu	dog	gòu	enough	gōu	ditch	
hěn	very	hèn	hate			
tāng	soup	táng	sugar			
tǎng	lie (down)	tàng	hot			
fēi	fly	fēn	cent, minute	fēng	wind	
gǎi	change	gěi	give			
kāi	open	hái	still			
néng	can	lěng	cold			
lóng	dragon	láng	wolf			
bái	white	bān	class			

当代中文

lái	come	lán	blue
nán	male	mǎn	full
màn	slow	máng	busy
hóng	red	gāo	high, tall
hēi	black		

V. Listen and repeat

kān mén	guard the door	kāi mén	open the door
hēibǎn	blackboard	hěn bái	very white
lǎohǔ	tiger	láodòng	work, labour
gǔdài	ancient	kǔhǎi	sea of bitterness
dédào	get	dàodé	morality
táopǎo	run away	bàodào	report for duty, check in
Běiměi	North America	měilì	beautiful
bāngmáng	lend a hand	bèndàn	fool
tóu téng	headache	ménkǒu	doorway
Hànyǔ	Chinese language		

0.4

I. Sound discrimination

1. Indicate which one you hear.

(1) A. jiā   B. qiā   [   ]

(2) A. jiǒng   B. qióng   [   ]

(3) A. gāo   B. jiào   [   ]

(4) A. kàn   B. quán   [   ]

(5) A. hǎo   B. xiǎo   [   ]

(6) A. qiú   B. qú   [   ]

(7) A. jiǔ   B. jǔ   [   ]

(8) A. xiān   B. xuān   [   ]

(9) A. qīn   B. qūn   [   ]

(10) A. jiě   B. jué   [   ]

(11) A. jiā   B. jiǎ   [   ]

(12) A.   xué   B.   xuě   [   ]

(13) A.   jiàng   B.   jiǎng   [   ]

(14) A.   xiào   B.   xiǎo   [   ]

2. Fill in the blanks with the initials you hear.

(1) _____ iē   (2) _____ iě   (3) _____ ián   (4) _____ iàn

(5) _____ íng   (6) _____ ǐng   (7) _____ īng   (8) _____ iā _____ íng

(9) _____ ué _____ iào (10) _____ iān _____ iáng

3. Fill in the blanks with the finals you hear.

(1)   b _____   (2)   p _____   (3)   d _____   (4)   n _____

(5)   l _____   (6)   x _____   (7)   x _____   (8)   q _____

(9)   j _____   (10) l _____ j _____   (11) b _____ j _____   (12) x _____ d _____

(13) j _____ j _____   (14) j _____ l _____   (15) q _____ x _____   (16) q _____ l _____

4. Mark the tones you hear.

(1) jiqi   (2) jiujing   (3) jianbing   (4) pinqiong   (5) mingliang   (6) lingdang

(7) qianmian   (8) mianbao   (9) qifen   (10) xiawu

5. Listen and write down the syllables you hear.

(1) _____   (2) _____   (3) _____   (4) _____

(5) _____   (6) _____   (7) _____   (8) _____

(9) _____   (10) _____   (11) _____   (12) _____

(13) _____   (14) _____   (15) _____   (16) _____

(17) _____   (18) _____

II. Listen and repeat

jiē	diē	qiē	tiē		
xī	xiē	xiān	xiāng		
yú	yuè	yuán			
jù	jiǔ	qù	qiú	xǔ	xiū
lán	liàn	láng	liàng		
máo	miáo	pào	piào		
xìn	xíng	xiàng	xióng		

III. Listen and repeat

yāo	waist	yáo	shake	yào	want
yóu	oil	yǒu	have	yòu	again
jiā	home	jiǎ	false	jià	holiday
xīng	star	xǐng	wake up	xíng	O.K.
xiǎng	think	xiàng	towards	xiāng	fragrant
yě	also	yè	night		
yān	smoke	yán	salt		
qiāo	knock	qiáo	bridge		
xiǎo	small	xiào	smile, laugh		
xiān	first	xián	salty		
tīng	listen	tíng	stop		
nián	year	niàn	read aloud		
nǎo	brain	niǎo	bird		
nán	male	nián	year		
niú	cow	nǚ	female		
qiē	cut	quē	lack		
xiě	write	xué	learn, study		
qiú	ball	jiǔ	alcoholic drink		
xióng	bear	qióng	poor, poverty-stricken		
yòng	use	yún	cloud		

当代中文

IV. Listen and repeat the following syllables, paying attention to the 3rd tone sandhi

kǒuyǔ	spoken language	yǒnggǎn	brave
měinǚ	beautiful woman	xiǎoniǎo	little bird
lǎojiā	hometown	kǎoyā	roast duck
diǎnxin	refreshments	jiǎngjīn	bonus
jiějué	solve	yǔyán	language
bǎohù	protect	fǎlǜ	law
kě'ài	lovely, cute	kěndìng	sure

V. Listen and repeat

yóuyǒng	swim		yǒuyòng	useful
jīqì	machine		qíjì	miracle, wonder
xūyào	need		xīyào	western medicine
juédìng	decide, decision		quèdìng	definite
quēdiǎn	shortcoming		quántiān	whole day
xuéxí	learn, study		xiūxi	rest
qīnwěn	kiss		qǐngwèn	Excuse me, may I ask...
jiéyuē	save (money, etc.)			
yuánliàng	forgive			
xuǎnjǔ	elect, election		xiàtiān	summer
jīntiān	today		míngtiān	tomorrow
qiūtiān	autumn		dōngtiān	winter
qùnián	last year		jīnnián	this year
míngnián	next year		xīnxiān	fresh
Měiguó	U.S.A.		Jiānádà	Canada
Yīngguó	U.K.		Àodàlìyà	Australia
xúnxù-jiànjìn	follow in order and advance step by step			
lóngténg-hǔyuè	dragons rising and tigers leaping; a scene of busting activity			

0.5

I. Sound discrimination

1. Indicate which one you hear.

(1) A. zì   B. cí   [   ]

(2) A. cū   B. zú   [   ]

(3) A. zì   B. jǐ   [   ]

(4) A. cí   B. qì   [   ]

(5) A. zūn   B. jūn   [   ]

(6) A. cuān   B. quán   [   ]

(7) A. cán   B. tán   [   ]

(8) A. sǎo   B. xiǎo   [   ]

(9) A. cǎo   B. qiáo   [   ]

(10) A. zǒu   B. zuò   [   ]

当代中文

(11) A. gān   B. guǎn   [   ]
(12) A. kěn   B. kǔn   [   ]
(13) A. kēi   B. kuī   [   ]
(14) A. cuò   B. cuō   [   ]
(15) A. wén   B. wèn   [   ]
(16) A. zuǐ   B. zuì   [   ]
(17) A. cí   B. cì   [   ]

2. Fill in the blanks with the initials you hear.

(1) _____ ā   (2) _____ iā   (3) _____ ān   (4) _____ ián
(5) _____ ǎo   (6) _____ iǎo   (7) _____ ì _____ í   (8) _____ ì _____ ī
(9) _____ í _____ ì   (10) _____ ī _____ ì   (11) _____ íng _____ í   (12) _____ íng _____ ì

3. Fill in the blanks with the finals you hear.

(1) k _____   (2) k _____   (3) k _____   (4) k _____
(5) k _____   (6) h _____   (7) h _____   (8) h _____
(9) h _____   (10) g _____   (11) g _____   (12) d _____
(13) d _____   (14) t _____   (15) t _____   (16) g _____ z _____
(17) c _____ c _____ (18) z _____ s _____ (19) c _____ g _____ (20) t _____ k _____
(21) h _____ l _____

4. Mark the tones you hear.

(1) kuajiang   (2) kuanguang   (3) tuola   (4) zuoye   (5) jisuan   (6) kuaisu
(7) nuanhuo   (8) cuican   (9) weida   (10) guojia   (11) huida   (12) wandan

5. Listen and write down the syllables you hear.

(1) _____   (2) _____   (3) _____   (4) _____
(5) _____   (6) _____   (7) _____   (8) _____
(9) _____

II. Listen and repeat

wā   wō   wài   wèi   wǎn   wěn
dū   dōu   duō   tú   tóu   tuó
gù   guà   guài   guān   guāng

hù	huà	huài	huán	huáng
zī	zū	cì	cù	sì	sù
zài	cài	sài		
zǎn	zāng	zěn		
cān	cáng	cēn		
zī	jī	cǐ	qī	sī	xī
zǎn	jiǎn			

第 0 课

III. Listen and repeat the following syllables, paying attention to the difference between u and ü

dùn	jūn	tún	qún	zǔ	jù	cù	qú
xuǎn	suàn	kuān	quán	zuān	juān		

IV. Listen and repeat

cāi	guess	cái	only	cài	dish
tuǐ	leg	tuī	push	tuì	retreat
suān	sour	suàn	calculate		
zuǐ	mouth	zuì	the most		
sān	three	sǎn	unbrella		
guā	melon	guà	hang		
dōu	all	duō	many		
guài	strange	kuài	fast		
zuò	do	zǒu	go, walk		
guó	country	gǒu	dog		

V. Listen and repeat the following syllables, paying attention to the 3rd tone sandhi

gǔdiǎn	classic	yǔfǎ	grammar
wǔdǎo	dancing	yǒuhǎo	friendly
liǎojiě	comprehend	yǒnggǎn	brave
yǔyī	raincoat	Běijīng	capital of China
yǐjīng	have (done sth.)		

当
代
中
文

Měiguó	U.S.A.	Fǎguó	France
hěn nán	very difficult		
bǐsài	competition	měilì	beautiful
jiǎn yàn	to test	cǎodì	meadow

VI. Listen and repeat

jīdàn	egg	zǐdàn	bullet		
jìsuàn	calculate	zìxuǎn	choose by oneself		
bízi	nose	bǐjì	note		
zìjǐ	oneself	cíqì	porcelain or china	sījī	driver
cānguān	visit, look around	tānguān	corrupt official		
qǐzǎo	get up early	tǐcāo	gymnastics		
cōngming	clever				
sēnlín	forest				

VII. Listen to the tape and practise the following sayings:

Wángpó mài guā, zì mài zì kuā.

Old lady Wang is boasting about the gourds she sells.

Máquè suī xiǎo, wǔzàng jù quán.

The sparrow may be small but it has all its vital organs.

Yǒu péng zì yuǎn fāng lái, bú yì lè hū?

Aren't you happy if there is a friend who comes from afar?

0.6

I. Sound discrimination

1. Indicate which one you hear.

(1) A. zhǐ   B. chí   [   ]

(2) A. zhì   B. zì   [   ]

(3) A. chí   B. cí   [   ]

(4) A. zhī   B. jī   [   ]

(5) A. chì   B. qì   [   ]

(6) A. shí   B. xí   [   ]

(7) A. rì   B. rè   [   ]

(8) A. chuān   B. quān   [   ]

(9) A. shào   B. xiào   [   ]

(10) A. shā   B. shān   C. shāng   [   ]

(11) A. chán   B. chuán   C. chuáng   [   ]

(12) A. chī   B. chē   C. chū   [   ]

(13) A. piāo   B. piǎo   C. piào   [   ]

(14) A. zhāng   B. zhǎng   C. zhàng   [   ]

(15) A. chōng   B. chóng   C. chòng   [   ]

(16) A. chū   B. chú   C. chù   [   ]

(17) A. cí   B. cǐ   C. cì   [   ]

2. Fill in the blanks with the initials you hear.

(1) ____ ī   (2) ____ ī   (3) ____ ì   (4) ____ ì

(5) ____ í   (6) ____ í   (7) ____ í   (8) ____ ǐ

(9) ____ ì   (10) ____ ǐ ____ ǒu   (11) ____ ūn ____ uāng   (12) ____ án ____ āo

(13) ____ āng ____ èng

3. Mark the tones you hear.

(1) shici   (2) turan   (3) caice   (4) zaoyu   (5) congrong (6) renming

(7) ruguo   (8) shuxi   (9) re'ai   (10) suanshu   (11) chize   (12) shishi

(13) zhunbei (14) shuiwen (15) chuli   (16) shencha

4. Listen and write down the syllables you hear.

(1) _____   (2) _____   (3) _____   (4) _____

(5) _____   (6) _____   (7) _____   (8) _____

(9) _____   (10) _____

II. Listen and repeat

zhī   chī   shī   jī   qī   xī   zī   cī   sī

zhā   zā   jiā

chā   cā   qiā

chuán   cuàn   quān

shāo   sǎo   xiào

rè   rì   lì

当代中文

III. Listen and repeat the following syllables, paying attention to retroflex finals

huār	flower	niǎor	bird
wánr	play	zhèr	here
nàr	there	nǎr	where

IV. Listen and repeat

shū	book	shǔ	count	shù	tree
zhù	live, stay	zhū	pig		
chuān	wear	chuán	boat		
chuáng	bed	chuāng	window		
shuǐ	water	shuí	who		
chūn	spring	chǔn	stupid		
shuō	say	shōu	receive		
shān	hill	sān	three		
zhǎo	look for	zǎo	early		
èr	two				

V. Listen and repeat

zhīdao	know	chídào	be late	qǐdǎo	pray
rúguǒ	if	lùguò	pass by		
shǎoshù	minority	xiǎoshù	small tree		
qìchē	car	qíchē	ride a bicycle		
shísì	fourteen	sìshí	forty		
róuruǎn	soft	tūrán	suddenly		
shāmò	desert	shénme	what		
shàngwǔ	morning	xiàwǔ	afternoon		
shuǐjiǎo	dumpling	shuìjiào	sleep		
róngyì	easy	rènyì	wantonly		
érzi	son	ěrduo	ear		
cèsuǒ	toilet	chùsuǒ	location		

Zhōngguó	China
shíshì-qiúshì	seek truth from facts, be practical and realistic
rénshān-rénhǎi	a sea of people
qīzuǐ-bāshé	all talking at once
shānqīng-shuǐxiù	green hills and clear waters
kāi yèchē	to work late into the night
yǎo ěrduo	to whisper in sb.'s ear
pāi mǎpì	to lick sb.'s boots

VI. Listen and practise the following sayings:

Bǎi wén bù rú yí jiàn.

It is better to see once than hear a hundred times.

Shībài shì chénggōng zhī mǔ.

Failure is the mother of success.

Cùn yǒu suǒ cháng, chǐ yǒu suǒ duǎn.

A foot may be too short in one case while an inch may be long enough in another. (Every person has his weak points as well as strong points.)

Dì-yī Kè   Nín Guìxìng
第一课   您贵姓
Lesson 1   What's Your Surname?

I. Read the following words and sentences

míngzi	name	míngjì	etch on one's mind
guó	country	gǒu	dog
jiào	call, shout	diào	drop
dōu	all, both	dú	poison

duō   many

bù hǎo

bù shuō Hànyǔ

bú shì Zhōngguórén

Wǒ bú xìng Wáng.

Wǒ bú jiào Wáng Yīng.

II. Words and structures

1. Substitution drills.

(1) A. 你是哪国人？

B. 我是中国人。

Jiānádà	Měiguó
加拿大	美国
Àodàlìyà	Yīngguó
澳大利亚	英国

(2) A. 她是中国人吗？

B. 她是中国人。

Jiānádà	Měiguó
加拿大	美国
Àodàlìyà	Yīngguó
澳大利亚	英国

(3) A. 你是不是中国人？

   B. 我不是中国人。

Jiānádà　　Měiguó
加拿大　　美国
Àodàlìyà　Yīngguó
澳大利亚　英国

(4) 您说英语还是说法语？

Zhāng　　　　Wáng
姓张 ……　　姓王
Zhāng Shān　Jiāng Shān
叫张山……叫江山

第一课

(5) 我是老师，他也是老师，我们都是老师。

Wáng
姓王
说汉语
不是中国人

2. **Fill in the blanks with the given words.**

　　是　说　姓　叫

(1) 他＿＿＿哪国人？

(2) 我＿＿＿马。

(3) 他＿＿＿什么名字？

(4) 她不＿＿＿汉语。

　　也　都

(5) 我是加拿大人，他＿＿＿是加拿大人，我们＿＿＿是加拿大人。

(6) 我不是中国人，他＿＿＿不是中国人，＿＿＿不是中国人。

　　吗　呢

(7) A: 您说英语＿＿＿？

   B: 我不说英语。您＿＿＿？

A: 我也不说英语。

3. **Turn the following affirmative sentences into negative sentences.**

   (1) 他是汉语老师。

   (2) 他说英语。

   (3) 他们都是加拿大人。

4. **Arrange the given words in the correct order to form a sentence.**

   (1) 我 美国 人 是

   (2) 她 美国 人 是 也

   (3) 他 美国 人 是 不

   (4) 你 叫 名字 什么

5. **Turn the following statements into 吗 questions and X 不 X questions.**

   (1) 他是我同学。

   (2) 他说汉语。

   (3) 他是张老师。

6. **Translate the following sentences into Chinese.**

   (1) I only speak Chinese.

   (2) What's your name?

   (3) Are you Chinese?

   (4) Do you speak English or French?

   (5) My surname is not Wang. My surname is Zhang.

III. Listening comprehension

1. What's the surname of the speaker?
2. Does he speak French?
3. What is their nationality?

4. What mistake did the boy make?

5. Is the girl Canadian or Chinese?

6. How many people were speaking? What are their names?

IV. Oral practice

1. Ask and answer the following questions with your classmates.

   What's your name?

   What's your nationality?

   Do you speak Chinese?

2. Introduce yourself: your name, your nationality, whether you can speak Chinese, your teacher's name.

3. Introduce one of your classmates.

V. Read the following passage and answer the questions

白小红，女，中国人，说汉语，也说英语。
王　英，女，加拿大华裔，说英语，也说一点儿汉语。
马力，男，澳大利亚人，说英语，不说法语。
江山，男，美国人，只说英语。
张老师，男，汉语老师。

How many people are there? What are their nationalities?

Who speaks Chinese? Who speaks English? Who speaks French?

VI. Fill in the table in Hanzi

姓名 xìngmíng name	性别 xìngbié sex	国籍 guójí nationality

Supplementary words

英国	(N.)	Yīngguó	the United Kingdom
华裔	(N.)	huáyì	person of Chinese ancestry who is not a Chinese citizen
一点儿		yìdiǎnr	a little
男	(Adj.)	nán	male
女	(Adj.)	nǚ	female

当代中文

第二课　认识你很高六

Lesson 2　Glad to Meet You

I. Read the following words

rènshi	know	piàoliang	beautiful
péngyou	friend	xǐhuan	like
shénme	what	míngzi	name
lǎoshī	teacher	pǔtōng	common
nǎ guó	which country	Měiguó	U.S.A.
qǐng zuò	Sit down, please.		
qǐng jìn	Come in, please.		

II. Words and structures

1. Substitution drills.

(1) 这是我的<u>女朋友</u>。

> 男朋友　　好朋友
> 老朋友　　老同学
> 汉语老师

(2) A: 你在哪儿学习？

B: 我在<u>林肯大学东亚学系</u>学习。

> Měiguó Huáshèngdùn　　Jiānádà Wòtàihuá
> 美国　华盛顿大学　　加拿大 渥太华大学
> Àodàlìyà　Xīní　　　Yīngguó Lúndūn
> 澳大利亚悉尼大学　　英国　伦敦大学

(3) A: 我可（以）不可以给你<u>打电话</u>?
    B: 可以。

发电子邮件
写信

(4) A: 东方学院怎么样?
    B: 东方学院<u>很大，也很好</u>。

很大，也很漂亮
不大，也不漂亮

(5) A: 请<u>进</u>!
    B: 好。谢谢!

坐
喝茶

2. **Fill in the blanks with the given words.**

　　　　打　发　喝　喜欢　认识　工作

(1) 我可以给你____电话吗?

(2) 我可以给你____电子邮件吗?

(3) 很高兴____你!

(4) 你在哪儿____?

(5) 请____茶。

3. **Arrange the given words in the correct order to form a sentence.**

(1) 我　　进出口公司　　在　　工作

(2) 他　　我们　　老师　　的　　是

(3) 我　　东亚学系　　　学生　　的　　是

(4) 我　　打电话　　可以　　吗　　给　你

4. **Complete the following sentences with the pattern "很+ Adj.".**

(1) 认识你我_____。

(2) 我的大学_____。

(3) 他的女朋友_____。

(4) 我的工作_____。

5. (1) Read the telephone numbers quickly.

5674932   2478321   9069543

24379067   21041796

(2) Write down the telephone numbers that you hear.

_____   _____   _____

_____   _____   _____

_____   _____

6. Translate the following sentences into Chinese.

(1) Glad to meet you!

(2) Come in, please!

(3) I study in the Dept. of East Asian Studies, Lincoln Univ.

(4) His girlfriend is beautiful.

(5) Their university is big, and beautiful too.

III. Listening comprehension

(1) Does he prefer telephone or e-mail?

(2) Did he hear the correct number?

(3) Is Mr. Zhang in?

(4) Is the man a teacher or a student?

(5) How is his university?

(6) Do all the students like their Chinese teacher?

(7) Are the two persons in the same city now?

IV. Oral practice

1. Ask and answer.

Exchange telephone numbers.

第二课

当代中文

2. Introduce yourself: where you are studying, how your university is, and whether you like your university or not.

3. Guess what the hostess is saying.

V. Read the following business card (名片 Míngpiàn) and answer the questions

北京大学中文系

江 力 教 授

地址：北京白马大街 134 号 405 室

电话：54647086(O)　51887976(H)

传真：54641890　电子邮件：jiangli@hotmail.com

Who is Prof. Jiang Li? Where does he work? Where does he live?

What's his telephone number and fax number?

VI. Write a short introduction about your university or college using the words provided

我　　　在……学习

好　　大　　漂亮　　喜欢

第二课

Supplementary words

华盛顿	(N.)	Huáshèngdùn	Washington
海德堡	(N.)	Hǎidébǎo	Heidelberg
悉尼	(N.)	Xīní	Sydney
伦敦	(N.)	Lúndūn	London
写	(V.)	xiě	write
信	(N.)	xìn	letter
名片	(N.)	míngpiàn	business card
北京	(N.)	Běijīng	(capital of China)
教授	(N.)	jiàoshòu	professor
地址	(N.)	dìzhǐ	address
街	(N.)	jiē	street
号	(MW)	hào	number
室	(N.)	shì	room
传真	(N.)	chuánzhēn	fax

当代中文

Dì-sān Kè   Nǐ Jiā Yǒu Jǐ Kǒu Rén

第三课   你家有几口人

Lesson 3   How Many People Are There in Your Family?

I. Read aloud the following phrases

shí yī	eleven		yì bǎi	one hundred
yì qiān	one thousand		yí wàn	ten thousand
yí gè rén	a person		yí suì	one year old
yì kǒu rén	a person (in a family)		yì jiā rén	the whole family
bàba	father		māma	mother
háizi	child(ren)		tàitai	wife
duōshao	how many, how much		dìfang	place
qù	go		qiú	beg, entreat
shǎo	few, little (in quantity)		xiǎo	small, little (in size)

II. Words and structures

1. Substitution drills.

(1) A: 你家有几口人?

B: 我家有四口人。

三 七 十

(2) A: 你们学校有多少学生?

B: 我们学校大概有三万个学生。

五百   两千
两千五百

(3) A: 他多大?

B: 他两岁。

十八岁   二十一岁
三十五岁

(4) A: 你为什么想学习汉语？

　　B: 因为<u>我有很多中国朋友</u>。

我喜欢汉语
我爷爷、奶奶在中国
我们在中国有一个公司
我想去中国工作
老板让我去中国工作

第三课

2. Fill in the blank with the words given.

个　口　岁

(1) 你有几____中国朋友？

(2) 我家有三____人。

(3) 我二十____。

几　多少

(4) 你们有____个汉语老师？

(5) 加拿大有____人？

两　二

(6) 我们班有____个汉语老师。

(7) 我们大学有十____个汉语老师。

3. Arrange the given words in the correct order to form a sentence.

(1) 你家　　口　　人　　几　　有

(2) 你　　个　　几　　中国　　朋友　　有

(3) 你们　　学校　　学生　　多少　　有

(4) 想　　我　　工作　　中国　　去

(5) 老板　　让　　去　　中国　　我　　工作

4. (1) Read the following numbers.

94 8597　　66 1185　　997 6100　　960 0000

65 0087　　106 8583　　154 0681　　13 0000 0000

当代中文

(2) Write down the numbers you hear.

_____   _____   _____

_____   _____   _____

_____   _____

5. Translate the following sentences into Chinese.

(1) He has two Chinese friends.

(2) He has a lot of Chinese friends.

(3) He has no Chinese friends.

(4) There is no teacher of Chinese in their university.

(5) There are many students of Chinese in our school.

(6) Are there any students learning Chinese in your school?

III. Listening comprehension

1. Is his wife here too? Yes.
2. Does he prefer sons or daughters? Both.
3. What does he think of her? Cute
4. How old do you think the man is? 64
5. What's the population of Shanghai? 176百
6. Why does he want to learn Chinese? his girlfriend's parents are chinese
7. Will he be sent to work in China by his company? no

IV. Oral practice

1. Ask and answer.

How many people are there in your school?

How many people are there in your family?

Why do you learn Chinese?

2. Introduce your family or school.

V. Read the following passage and answer the questions

我们学校有两万多个学生，有一百多个人学习汉语。我们学校很大，也很漂亮。我非常喜欢我们学校。

我们的汉语老师是女的，姓王。王老师是上海人，她先生也是我们学校的老师，是东亚系教授。他们有两个孩子。小孩子十一岁，上小学；大孩子十九岁，上大学，是我的同学。王老师和她先生的普通话都很好。但是，他们的孩子汉语很不好。

How many students are there in their university?

How many students are learning Chinese?

How many people are there in Prof. Wang's family?

How is their Chinese?

VI. Write a short passage to introduce your family or your school beginning with 我家有 …… or 我们学校有 ……

当代中文

Supplementary words

爷爷	(N.)	yéye	grandpa
奶奶	(N.)	nǎinai	grandma
多	(Particle)	duō	more than
非常	(Adv.)	fēicháng	very, very much
教授	(N.)	jiàoshòu	professor
先生	(N.)	xiānsheng	mister, husband

第四课

Dì-sì Kè　　Zhè Zhāng Dìtú Shì Yīngwén de
第四课　这 张 地图是 英文 的

Lesson 4　This Map Is in English

I. Read aloud the following phrases

zhèr	here	nàr	there
nǎr	where	wánr	play
cídiǎn	dictionary	cítiě	magnet
shuí	who	shuǐ	water
zhīdao	know	zhǐdǎo	guide, direct
qǐngwèn	Excuse me	qīnwěn	kiss
yǒuyòng	useful	yóuyǒng	swim
shàngkè	have classes	chànggē	sing songs

II. Words and structures

1. Substitution drills.

(1) A: 我看一下，行吗?

　　B: 行。

用	借

(2) 这两张地图都是英文的。

中文
法文

(3) 哪本词典是老师的?

本	书	支	笔
个	本子		

(4) 这本词典非常<u>好</u>。

大　有用
漂亮

2. Fill in the blanks with the words given.

问　用　玩儿　知道

(1) 我想去北京_____。

(2) 他在哪个教室上课，你_____吗？

(3) 请_____，这是您的词典吗？

(4) 我可不可以_____一下您的词典？

本　张　个　支　下

(5) 让我看一_____你的中国地图，可以吗？

(6) 这_____词典很有用。

(7) 那_____本子是谁的？

(8) 我有两_____加拿大地图。

(9) 这_____书很有意思。

(10) 请给我一_____笔，好吗？

3. Complete the following sentences.

那个地方_____，_____。（大　漂亮）

他 英语_____，法语_____。（好）

他们学校老师_____，学生_____。（少　多）

4. Translate the following sentences into Chinese.

(1) I like this one. I don't like that one.

(2) This map of China is very useful.

(3) This dictionary is very good.

(4) Could I use your dictionary?

(5) Whose are these two dictionaries?

III. Listening comprehension

(1) What does he have?   *2*

(2) Whose dictionary is it?   *his teacher's*

(3) Why does the man want to look at the map of China?   *wants to visit Beijing*

(4) What does the woman think of the book?   *interesting*

(5) Does the woman lend her dictionary to the man?   *no*

(6) What kind of a map did the man want to look at?   *English chinese map*

(7) Why does the boy think that Chinese is useful?   *in China it's useful*

第四课

IV. Oral practice

1. Ask and answer.

Do you have a map of China? Is the map in English or in Chinese?

Do you have a dictionary? What dictionary is it? Is it useful?

2. Try to borrow a map or a dictionary from your classmate.

V. Read the following passage and answer the questions   ✗

中国在东半球,加拿大在西半球。加拿大很大,中国也很大。中国人口多,加拿大人口不多。中国人说汉语,加拿大人说英语或者法语。中国人学习英语,加拿大人学习汉语。中国人说英语很好学,加拿大人说汉语不好学。

What's the difference between Canada and China?

VI. Write a short commentary about a map or a dictionary beginning with 我有 ……

(words for reference: 这   好   大   有用   漂亮)

当代中文

Supplementary words

东半球	(N.)	dōngbànqiú	the Eastern Hemisphere
西半球	(N.)	xībànqiú	the Western Hemisphere
或者	(Conj.)	huòzhě	or
人口	(N.)	rénkǒu	population
好学		hǎo xué	easy to learn

Dì-wǔ Kè   Néng bu Néng   Shì Yi Shì
第五课   能 不 能   试一试
Lesson 5   May I Try Them On?

第
五
课

I. Read the following words and sentences

买	mǎi	buy		卖	mài	sell		
千	qiān	thousand		钱	qián	money		
吃	chī	eat		迟	chí	late		
最	zuì	the most		嘴	zuǐ	mouth		
菜	cài	dish		猜	cāi	guess		
要	yào	want		腰	yāo	waist		
会	huì	can		灰	huī	ash	回	huí	be back

睡觉 shuìjiào sleep　　　　水饺 shuǐjiǎo dumpling, Chinese ravioli
房间 fángjiān room　　　　饭店 fàndiàn restautrant

这件白衬衫多少钱? Zhè jiàn bái chènshān duōshao qián?
这条也太大。 Zhè tiáo yě tài dà.
你要酸辣汤? Nǐ yào suānlàtāng?
对，我要酸辣汤。 Duì, wǒ yào suānlàtāng.

II. Words and structures

1. Substitution drills.

(1) A: 你会说汉语吗?
　　B: 我会说一点儿汉语。

说……法语	写……汉字

当
代
中
文

(2) A: <u>这件白衬衫</u>多少钱?

B: 一百五十块。

那条裤子
这件衣服
那本书

(3) A: 能不能<u>试一试</u>?

B: 当然可以。

看一看　问一问
用一用　休息休息

(4) 那是他们饭店<u>最好吃</u>的菜。

贵
便宜

(5) 这个菜<u>很</u>辣。

不　　不太
比较　非常

2. Fill in the blanks with the given words.

和　也　还

(1) 我要买衬衫_____裤子。

(2) 我想买一件衬衫,他_____想买一件衬衫。

(3) 我想买一件衬衫,_____想买一条裤子。

3. Fill in the blanks with different adjectives.

(1) 这个饭店的菜非常_____。

(2) 这条裤子很_____。

(3) 两百块? 太_____了!

(4) 这是一本非常_____的书。

(5) 我不喜欢这件白衬衫,我喜欢那件_____衬衫。

(6) 我喜欢吃_____的,不喜欢吃_____的。

4. Translate the following sentences into Chinese.

(1) I can speak a little Chinese.

(2) Can I have a try?

(3) What do you want, sir?

(4) This dish tastes good.

(5) I like to go shopping in small shops.

(6) There is a very big shop there.

III. Listening comprehension

(1) Can he speak Chinese very well?

(2) How much is the shirt?

(3) Which one does he want?

(4) Where are they?

(5) Why are the dishes so expensive in this restautrant?

(6) Which places do they prefer to go shopping? Why?

(7) Are they satisfied with the dishes?

第
五
课

IV. Oral practice

1. Buy a coat in a shop. Ask the price, and choose the right colour and size. The shop assistant may make some snggestions.

2. **Read the menu [càidān] and order the dishes [diǎn cài]. The waitress may make some suggestions.**

菜 单

菜

烤鸭　　糖醋鱼　　麻辣豆腐

鱼香肉丝　青椒牛肉　炒青菜

汤

酸辣汤　　　番茄鸡蛋汤

点心

水饺　　　　馄饨

小笼包　　　炒面

鱼香肉丝	yúxiāngròusī	sautéed shredded pork in hot sauce
麻辣豆腐	máládòufu	bean curd in chili and wild pepper sauce
烤	kǎo	roast
鸭	yā	duck
青椒	qīngjiāo	green pepper
炒	chǎo	fried
青菜	qīngcài	green vegetables
番茄	fānqié	tomato
鸡蛋	jīdàn	egg
面	miàn	noodle

V. Read the following passage and answer the questions

　　有很多不同的中国菜。广东菜和四川菜不一样，上海菜和山东菜不一样，中国的中国菜和美国的中国菜也不太一样。不同的地方有不同的菜，不同的人喜欢不同的味道。有的人喜欢吃甜的，有的人喜欢吃咸的，有的人喜欢吃酸的，有的人喜欢吃辣的。在中国，有很多人喜欢吃辣的。有人说：四川人不怕辣，湖南人辣不怕，江西人怕不辣。你想想：谁最喜欢吃辣的？

Are there different flavour of dishes in different parts of China?

People from which places like hot dishes very much?

VI. Write a short passage beginning with: 在这儿，有很多中国饭店。……

(words for reference: 菜　菜的名字　知道　会　菜单　因为　认识　好吃

喜欢　酸　辣　甜)

第五课

Supplementary words

写	(V.)	xiě	write
休息	(V.)	xiūxi	have a rest
不同	(Adj.)	bùtóng	different
一样	(Adj.)	yíyàng	same
味道	(N.)	wèidao	taste
广东	(N.)	Guǎngdōng	
四川	(N.)	Sìchuān	
上海	(N.)	Shànghǎi	
山东	(N.)	Shāndōng	
有的	(Pron.)	yǒude	some
甜	(Adj.)	tián	sweet
咸	(Adj.)	xián	salty
怕	(V.)	pà	be afraid of
湖南	(N.)	Húnán	
江西	(N.)	Jiāngxī	
菜单	(N.)	càidān	menu

Dì-liù Kè   Míngtiān Dǎsuàn   Gàn Shénme
第六课 明天 打算 干什么
Lesson 6   What Are You Going to Do Tomorrow?

I. Read the following words and sentences

上午	shàngwǔ	morning	下午	xiàwǔ	afternoon
休息	xiūxi	rest	学习	xuéxí	study
打算	dǎsuàn	plan	大蒜	dàsuàn	garlic
接	jiē	meet	见	jiàn	see
一半	yíbàn	half	一般	yìbān	general

我想去打球。   Wǒ xiǎng qù dǎqiú.

我要去看一个朋友。   Wǒ yào qù kàn yí gè péngyou.

明天晚上我有一个约会。   Míngtiān wǎnshang wǒ yǒu yí gè yuēhuì.

II. Words and structures

1. Substitution drills.

(1) A: 今天星期几?

B: 今天星期一。

星期二	星期三	星期四
星期五	星期六	星期天

(2) A: 现在几点?

B: 现在八点。

九点三刻   十点半
十一点二十分

(3) A: 明天晚上你打算干什么？
　　B: 我明天晚上<u>有一个约会</u>。

要去看一个朋友
要做功课
要去打工
在家里休息

喝茶　打球
看电影

(4) A: 我想请你一起去<u>喝咖啡</u>。
　　B: 好的，谢谢！

(5) A: 明天下午两点半我在<u>咖啡馆</u>等你。
　　B: 好，明天见！

学校　家里
公园门口

第六课

2. **Arrange the given words in the correct order to form a sentence.**

(1) 有空儿③　你①　下午②　吗④

(2) 我①　去④　看⑥　你⑤　晚上③　明天②

(3) 休息⑤　我①　明天②　家里④　在③

(4) 我们①　见面⑤　晚上九点②　咖啡馆④　在③

(5) 我①　他④　去⑤　打球⑥　想②　请③　*guǎn*　coffee bar / shop

3. **Fill in the blanks with the words given.**

打　喝　做　看　休息

(1) 你喜欢_____什么球？

(2) 今天星期天，他在家里_____。

(3) 我不喜欢_____电视。

(4) 今天晚上我要_____很多功课。

(5) 要不要_____咖啡？

当代中文

4. What time is it now?

5. Translate the following sentences into Chinese.

(1) What are you going to do tomorrow morning?

(2) I'm very busy today.

(3) I will be waiting for you at home at 2:30 tomorrow afternoon.

(4) He invited me to have dinner with him this evening.

III. Listening comprehension

(1) What time is it now?

(2) What will he do this evening?

(3) What does the man mean?

(4) What will she do tomorrow?

(5) What will he do tomorrow?

(6) Does the girl accept the boy's invitation?

(7) Where and when will they meet?

IV. Oral practice

1. Ask and answer.

What day of the week is today?

What time is it now?

What will you do tomorrow?

2. Look at the pictures and answer the questions.

When does he get up (qǐchuáng, 起床 get up)?

When does he have breakfast? (chī zǎofàn, 吃早饭 have breakfast)

When does he go to school? (qù shàngxué, 去上学 go to school)

When does he have supper? (chī wǎnfàn, 吃晚饭 have supper)

When does he go to bed? (shuìjiào, 睡觉 go to bed)

(1)

(2)

(3)

第六课

(4)

(5)

3. A calls B to invite him to go drink coffee/ go to the movie.

(1) B accepts the invitation but wants to change the time.

(2) B tries to find an excuse and refuse the invitation.

V. Read the following passage and answer the questions

　　我平时很忙。白天要上课,晚上还要做功课。我的中国朋友请我去玩儿,可是,我哪有空儿? 谢天谢地,明天星期六,没有课了。可是,我明天上午、下午都要去打工。我爸爸、妈妈让我在家里休息休息,可是,我要去打工。因为,我不喜欢用爸爸、妈妈的钱。后天是星期天,我上午要去机场接一位朋友,下午去打球,晚上有一个约会。你看,星期六、星期天,我也很忙。

What does he do during the weekdays?

What will he do tomorrow?

What will he do the day after tomorrow?

VI. Write down your plans for tomorrow

第

六

课

Supplementary words

电影	diànyǐng	movie
咖啡馆	kāfēiguǎn	café
公园	gōngyuán	park
门口	ménkǒu	entrance, doorway
平时	píngshí	ordinarily, usually
可是	kěshì	but
谢天谢地	xiètiān-xièdì	thank heaven
后天	hòutiān	the day after tomorrow
机场	jīchǎng	airport

Dì-qī Kè   Nǐ Shénme Shíhou Huílai

第七课　你什么时候回来

Lesson 7　When Will You Come Back?

I. Read the following words and sentences

长	cháng	long	强	qiáng	strong
找	zhǎo	look for	叫	jiào	call
旅行	lǚxíng	travel	流行	liúxíng	popular, fashionable
眼镜	yǎnjìng	glasses, spectacles	眼睛	yǎnjing	eye
进去	jìnqu	go in	进出	jìnchū	go in and out

你找谁？	Nǐ zhǎo shuí?
他刚出去。	Tā gāng chūqu.
我想去中国旅行。	Wǒ xiǎng qù Zhōngguó lǚxíng.
我七月一号以前回来。	Wǒ qīyuè yī hào yǐqián huílai.

II. Words and structures

1. Substitution drills.

(1) A: 今天几号？

B: 今天<u>十月一号</u>。

一月二号　四月五号
十二月二十五号

(2) A: 你打算什么时候回来？

B: 我打算<u>七月一号</u>以前回来。

三点钟　吃饭
明年四月

(3) A: <u>放假</u>以后你去哪儿?
　　 B: 我回家。

四点钟　下课
一个星期

(4) 他<u>高高的，瘦瘦的</u>。

胖胖的，白白的。
矮矮的，瘦瘦的。
高高大大的。

第
七
课

(5) 他有点儿<u>担心</u>。

忙　累
不高兴

2. Fill in the blanks with the words given.

　　穿　戴
(1) 他喜欢_____红衬衫。
(2) 她每天都_____牛仔裤。
(3) 他_____眼镜吗?

　　还是　或者
(4) 你这个月去_____下个月去?
(5) 我打算今天下午去，_____明天上午去。

　　回　回来　回去
(6) 我家在北京，放假以后我要_____北京。
(7) 我家在北京，放假以后我打算_____看看我的家人。
(8) 他上个月去北京了，昨天刚_____。

　　一点儿　有点儿
(9) 我会说_____汉语。
(10) 我想喝_____水。
(11) 他今天_____不高兴。
(12) 那儿的东西_____贵。

不　别

(13) 我没有空儿，_____能去旅行。

(14) 那个商店的东西太贵，你_____去那儿买。

3. Fill in the blanks with the reduplicated forms of the given adjectives (followed by 的).

(1) 她___高高的___（高），头发___长长的___（长）。

(2) 这个汤___酸酸的___（酸），___辣辣的___（辣），真好喝。

4. Look at the pictures and guess what the man is saying.

(1)

你_____！

(2)

你_____！

(3)

你_____！

5. Translate the following sentences into Chinese.

(1) I will come again in a short while.

(2) He has just gone out.

(3) I will come back before the 4th of the next month.

(4) All of the teachers there are females.

III. Listening comprehension

(1) What did the man say?

(2) Is the man the one the woman wants to see?

(3) When will he go traveling?

(4) Where are the two people talking?

(5) Why couldn't the man read the character?

(6) Do the students have holidays during Christmas?

(7) What does the man worry about?

IV. Oral practice

1. Read Wang Ying's schedule and talk about it to your classmates in Chinese.

May 26	trip to Beijing, Shanghai and Xi'an
June 26	back

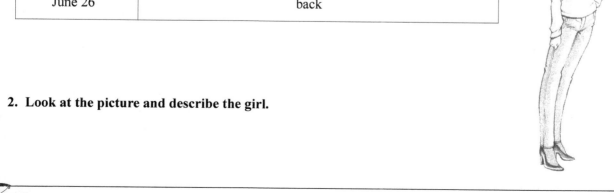

2. Look at the picture and describe the girl.

第七课

当代中文

V. Read the following passage and answer the questions

王老师：

　　您好！我来找您，可是您不在。

　　放假以后我打算去北京旅行，但是我没有北京地图。我不知道在什么地方可以买北京地图。您有北京地图吗？如果您有，我可以不可以用一下？

　　还有，您在北京有没有朋友？我去北京以后，他们能不能帮助我？

　　晚上我给您打电话。谢谢！

江山

3 月 21 日

Who wrote this? To whom was it written? When was it written?

Why does Jiang Shan want to see Prof. Wang?

VI. Suppose you will go traveling in China. Please e-mail your friend in China to tell him when you will arrive and your flight number, and ask your friend to meet you at the airport.

1. Words for your reference.

航班	hángbān	flight number	到	dào	arrive
飞机	fēijī	plane	机场	jīchǎng	airport
接	jiē	meet, pick up			

2. Your e-mail should begin with the following sentence.

张明：

　　你好！我打算……

第七课

Supplementary words

胖	pàng	fat
矮	ǎi	short (in height)
累	lèi	tired
但是	dànshì	but
如果	rúguǒ	if

当代中文

Dì-bā Kè   Fùjìn Yǒu Méiyǒu Yínháng

第八课　附近 有 没有 银行

Lesson 8　Is There a Bank Nearby?

I. Read the following words and sentences

前面	qiánmiàn	in front of	见面	jiànmiàn	meet (each other)
从	cóng	from	同	tóng	together with
骑车	qí chē	ride bicycles	汽车	qìchē	automobile, car
怎么	zěnme	how	什么	shénme	what
客气	kèqi	polite	科技	kējì	science and technology
车站	chēzhàn	stop, station	出站	chū zhàn	exit the station
地铁	dìtiě	subway, metro	电梯	diàntī	elevator

向左拐，过马路。　　　　Xiàng zuǒ guǎi, guò mǎlù.

邮局就在那个银行的旁边。　Yóujú jiù zài nàge yínháng de pángbiān.

能不能坐公共汽车去？　　Néng bu néng zuò gōnggòng qìchē qù?

II. Words and structures

1. Substitution drills.

(1) <u>附近</u>有没有银行?

前面
你家附近
学校旁边

(2) 邮局就在<u>那个银行的旁边</u>。

汽车站的前面
我们学校的后面
他们公司的右面
那个商店的左面

(3) 地铁站离<u>汽车站</u>远不远？

这儿　你家
你们公司

(4) 能不能骑<u>自行车</u>去？

坐飞机
坐火车
坐公共汽车
坐地铁

第八课

2. Fill in the blanks with the words given.

怎么　怎么样　什么

(1) 请问，去邮局＿＿＿＿＿走？

(2) "Desk" 汉语＿＿＿＿＿说？

(3) 那个饭店＿＿＿＿＿？

(4) 那是＿＿＿＿＿词典？

(5) 你明天打算干＿＿＿＿＿？

(6) 你的工作＿＿＿＿＿？

(7) 这个字＿＿＿＿＿写？

离　从

(8) 这儿＿＿＿＿＿市中心远不远？

(9) ＿＿＿＿＿这儿到市中心远不远？

(10) ＿＿＿＿＿银行到邮局很近。

(11) 银行＿＿＿＿＿邮局很近。

在　有

(12) 请问，附近＿＿＿＿＿邮局吗？

(13) 银行旁边＿＿＿＿＿一个邮局。

(14) 邮局＿＿＿＿＿我家左面。

(15) 汽车站就＿＿＿＿＿地铁站旁边。

(16) 大学门口就_____一个饭店。

3. Write 在 **sentences that match the pictures.**

e.g.:

词典在桌子上。

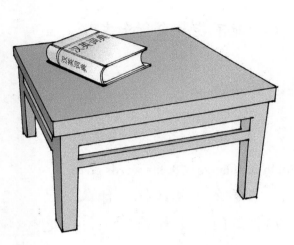

(1)

马力

江山

(2)

第
八
课

(3)

4. Write 有 sentences that match the pictures.

e.g.:

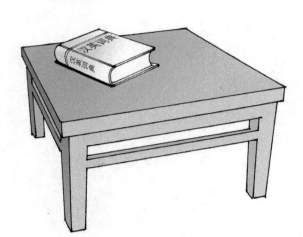

桌子上有一本词典。

5. Translate the following sentences into Chinese.

(1) Is there a post office nearby?

(2) There is a bookstore in front of my home.

(3) The subway station is not far away from the bus stop.

(4) Go ahead, turn left, cross a road, and there is a bank.

(5) I will go there by bike.

III. Listening comprehension

1. Is it far from his home to his school?

2. By what means will he go?

3. Where does he want to go?

4. What are they discussing?

5. Is there a subway station at the gate of the school?

6. Circle the place where the Bank of China is.

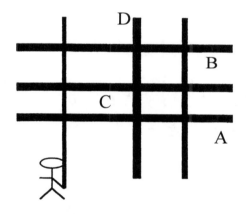

7. Mark the route to the railway station.

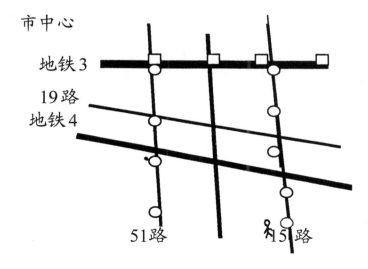

IV. Oral practice

Describe the route to the university for Jack.

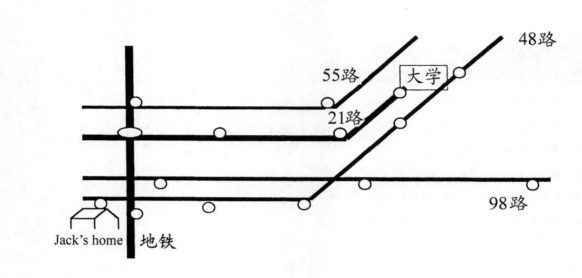

Words for reference:

先　坐　地铁　然后　换　公共汽车　到　终点站 zhōngdiǎnzhàn terminus, last stop 或者　坐　下车　以后　走一点儿

V. Read the following passage and answer the questions

　　我家在市中心。我家前面有商店、书店、水果店、食品店、饭店，我家左面有一个银行，我家右面有一个邮局。我爸爸在左面的银行工作，我妈妈在右面的邮局工作。我常常去前面的商店买东西。我的学校就在我家后面。从我家到学校很近。不用坐公共汽车，也不用开车，只要走过去就行。

Where is his house?

What's on the left of his house?

What's on the right of his house?

What's behind his house?

What's in front of his house?

Where is his school?

How does he get there?

VI. Write down what you said in the oral practice of exercise IV

第八课

Supplementary words

飞机	(N.)	fēijī	plane
火车	(N.)	huǒchē	train
桌子	(N.)	zhuōzi	desk
水果	(N.)	shuǐguǒ	fruit
食品	(N.)	shípǐn	food
不用	(Op. V.)	bú yòng	needn't
开车		kāi chē	drive a car
常常	(Adv.)	chángcháng	often

Dì-jiǔ Kè   Wǒ Yǐqián Yǎngguo Niǎor

第九课   我以前养过鸟儿

Lesson 9   I've Raised Birds Before

I. Words and structures

1. Read aloud the following phrases.

养花儿   养动物   养狗   养猫   养鸟   养鱼

有麻烦   很麻烦   太麻烦了   麻烦你了

有的人   有的东西   有的地方   有的时候

对他很熟悉   对这个字不熟悉   对这些地方不熟悉

有时间   没有时间   多长时间/多少时间   时间很长   时间还早

我自己   他自己   我们自己   自己的事儿   自己的钱

2. Substitution drills.

(1)   我以前养过花儿。

狗	猫
鸟	鱼

(2)   以前不可以养狗，现在可以了。

知道
会说汉语
喜欢打球
戴眼镜

(3) 听说，你要<u>去北京</u>了？

去中国旅行

办公司

换工作

(4) 要是你<u>想去</u>的话，我<u>陪你一起去</u>。

想拍照 …… 可以帮你拍

明天有空儿 …… 请你吃饭

没有地图 …… 给你一张

(5) 你得<u>给我买飞机票</u>。

告诉我怎么走

给家里打个电话

问问别人

3. Fill in the blanks with the words given.

办　　熟悉　　登　　拍

(1) 公司让我去那儿_____点儿事。

(2) 能不能请您给我们_____一张照片？

(3) 他喜欢_____山。

(4) 他对中国很_____。

件　　张　　个　　只

(5) 我想买一_____到北京的飞机票。

(6) 今天晚上我要办两_____事儿。

(7) 那_____地方我没去过。

(8) 他家以前养过一_____猫。

4. Complete the following dialogues with the 没（…）V. 过（Obj.） **pattern.**

(1) 那家饭店的菜好吃吗？

　　　不知道。我_____(在那儿吃)

(2) 这个字你认识吗?

不认识。我们_____(学)

(3) 他现在在北京还是在上海?

不知道。他去中国以后,_____(给我打电话),

也_____(给我发电子邮件)

5. Complete the sentences with "……了" to denote a change of situation.

(1) 我以前不会说汉语,现在_____。

(2) 那儿的东西以前很便宜,现在_____。

(3) 他以前非常爱他的太太,现在_____。

(4) 这个城市以前没有地铁,现在_____。

6. Translate these sentences into Chinese.

(1) I don't like it any more.

(2) I haven't been there before.

(3) It is said that he will go to Beijing next month.

(4) I'll go with you if I have time.

(5) Some like raising dogs; some like raising birds; some like raising fish.

II. Listening comprehension

For each conversation, choose an appropriate answer for the second person after you have listened to what the first person says.

(1) A. 以前养过。

B. 我家两口人。

C. 鸟儿很有意思。

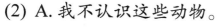

(2) A. 我不认识这些动物。

B. 他喜欢养小动物。

C. 我对这儿不熟悉。

(3) A. 怎么没去过？

B. 我不想去了。

C. 那儿不太长。

(4) A. 你去北京干什么？

B. 坐飞机还是坐汽车？

C. 你要什么时候的？

(5) A. 很麻烦。

B. 没关系。

C. 谢谢你！

(6) A. 欢迎你去。

B. 你陪我去吧。

C. 你家远不远？

(7) A. 这本词典很好，很有用。

B. 对不起，我现在没有时间。

C. 对不起，我自己要用。

(8) A. 你找谁？

B. 当然可以。

C. 你要哪张？

当代中文

III. Oral practice

1. Question and answer drill with your classmates.

(1) 你以前最喜欢什么？现在呢？

(2) 你去过哪些地方？还想再去吗？为什么？

2. Talk about a hobby of yours.

IV. Reading comprehension

Read the following passage and answer the questions that follow.

> 我喜欢旅行，但是去过的地方不多。我没去过中国，也没登过长城。我早就听说过中国的长城，听说过"不到长城非好汉"这句话，很想去登一登长城，做一个"好汉"。我上大学的时候，每年放假以后，有很多时间。但是，那时候我没有很多钱，我得打工挣钱，所以不能去旅行。现在，我工作了，有钱了，但是，我没有时间了，还是不能去。真是太遗憾了！

第九课

Answer these questions.

    1. 他去过北京吗？

    2. 他知道长城吗？

    3. 他想不想去中国？

    4. 他为什么一直没去？
               straight

V. Writing exercise

Write a short paragraph about a hobby of yours.

当代中文

Supplementary words

动物园	(N.)	dòngwùyuán	zoo
句	(M.W.)	jù	sentence
话	(N.)	huà	words, speech
挣钱	(V.O.)	zhèng qián	to earn money
一直	(Adv.)	yìzhí	continuously, always, all along
遗憾	(Adj.)	yíhàn	pity
爱好	(N., V.)	àihào	hobby; to be fond of

Dì-shí Kè　　Tā Qù Yīyuàn le
第十课　她去医院了

Lesson 10　She Has Gone to the Hospital

I. Words and structures

1. Read aloud the following phrases.

已经来了　　已经到了　　已经知道了　　已经放假了　　已经休息了

还在学习　　还想买一点儿　　还没到　　还没工作　　还不知道

很可能　　不可能　　有可能　　可能知道　　可能不去　　不可能去

睡睡觉　　睡过觉　　睡了一觉　　睡个好觉

说完　　吃完　　喝完　　学完　　看完　　做完　　用完　　卖完

错了　　说错了　　写错了　　做错了　　走错了

肚子疼　　上厕所　　去医院　　看病　　看医生

2. Substitution drills.

(1) 他现在不在家，他去医院了。

| 朋友家　商店 |
| 公司　学校 |

(2) A: 大家都来了没有？
　　B: 王英没来，别的同学都来了。

| 到　　去 |
| 写　　看 |

(3) A: 今天早上你吃了什么？
　　B: 今天早上我吃了几片面包。

| 一个水果　一个面包 |
| 两个鸡蛋　两个包子 |
| 一碗米饭　一碗面条 |

当代中文

(4) A: 你想，现在她在干什么？

B: 现在她可能正在吃早饭。

睡觉	看书
看电视	喝咖啡

(5) A: 你是不是吃了不干净的东西？

B: 这怎么可能呢？

昨天上午没去上课

在那家店里买过衣服

不会骑自行车

3. **Fill in the blanks with the words given.**

新鲜   干净   着急   舒服   疼

(1) 这个城市的马路非常_____。

(2) 他等了十分钟，菜还没来，他有点儿_____了。

(3) 昨天晚上没好好儿睡觉，今天有点儿头_____。

(4) 你哪儿不_____？头疼还是肚子疼？

(5) 这个面包是上个星期的，不_____。

4. **Arrange the given words in the correct order to form a sentence.**

(1) 他 起床 了 已经 肯定

(2) 我 说 没 还 完

(3) 你 进出口公司 在 工作 是不是

(4) 他 吃晚饭 的 每天 在 饭店 学校旁边

(5) 我　给我朋友　昨天　打　一个　电话　了

5. Translate these sentences into Chinese.

(1) He is having his breakfast right now.

(2) I bought a red shirt yesterday.

(3) The bus hasn't come yet.

(4) I get up at six o'clock every day.

(5) She feels a bit uncomfortable.

第
十
课

II.　Listening comprehension

Listen to each conversation, then choose an appropriate answer to each question.

(1) A. 在医院　　　B. 在商店　　　C. 在饭店

(2) A. 往里走　　　B. 往左拐　　　C. 往右拐

(3) A. 他病了　　　B. 他是医生　　　C. 他朋友病了

(4) A. 他要去吃晚饭

　　　B. 他还没吃早饭

　　　C. 他刚刚吃完早饭

(5) A. 因为这些水果不新鲜，所以不要钱。

　　　B. 要是这些水果不新鲜的话，他就不要钱。

　　　C. 这些水果很新鲜，但是他想请客，所以不要钱。

当代中文

(6) A. 小王说过他想跟他们一起去。

B. 他们还要等一等小王。

C. 小王肯定已经去那儿了。

(7) A. 面包、牛肉和鱼

B. 面条、米饭和衣服

C. 面包、牛奶、鱼和肉

III. Oral practice

1. Look at each picture and speak about what the people are doing.

图1

图2

图3

图4

图5

第 十 课

2. Question and answer drill with your classmates.

(1) 同学们都来了吗？

(2) 你昨天晚上学习汉语了没有？

(3) 你昨天干什么了？

(4) 昨天这个时候，你在干什么？

(5) 明天这个时候，你大概在干什么？

IV. Reading comprehension

Read the passage and answer the questions that follow.

请假条

金老师：

　　我感冒了，身体不舒服，头疼，咳嗽，还有点儿发烧。昨天下午我去医院看了医生。医生说，我得吃药，还得打针。医生告诉我，感冒以后，要多喝水，多睡觉。他让我休息两天。所以，今天和明天我不能上课了。对不起！

王 英

1月20日

当代中文

请假条

金老师：
　　我感冒了，身体不舒服，头疼，咳嗽，还有点儿发烧。昨天下午我去医院看了医生。医生说，我得吃药，还得打针。医生告诉我，感冒以后，要多喝水，多睡觉。他让我休息两天。所以，今天和明天我不能上课了。对不起！

　　　　　　　　　　　　　　王英
　　　　　　　　　　　　　　1月20日

Answer these questions.

1. 王英今天怎么啦？

2. 她去过医院没有？

3. 医生让她休息几天？

V. Writing exercise

Write a note requesting a leave of absence.

第
十
课

Supplementary words

水果	(N.)	shuǐguǒ	fruit
鸡蛋	(N.)	jīdàn	chicken egg
包子	(N.)	bāozi	steamed, stuffed bun
碗	(N.)	wǎn	bowl
面条	(N.)	miàntiáo	noodles
感冒	(V.)	gǎnmào	to catch cold
身体	(N.)	shēntǐ	body, health
咳嗽	(V.)	késou	to cough
发烧	(V.)	fāshāo	to have a fever
打针	(V.O.)	dǎ zhēn	to give/get an injection
请假条	(N.)	qǐngjiàtiáo	written request for a leave of absence

当代中文

Dì-shíyī Kè   Tāmen Shì Shénme Shíhou Lái de

第十一课   他们是什么时候来的

Lesson 11   When Did They Come?

I.   Words and structures

1. Read aloud the following phrases.

坐火车   坐飞机   坐汽车

中国历史   中国文化   中国经济

参观博物馆   参观一个学校   参观一个公司

做生意   谈生意   生意不错   生意很好

对动物有兴趣   对动物没有兴趣   对动物很感兴趣

新书   新学校   新老师   新学生   新汽车   新衣服

跟他借一本词典   借一本词典给他   借给他一本词典

2. Substitution drills.

(1) 他们是<u>什么时候</u>来的？

> 怎么
> 从哪儿
> 跟谁一起

(2) 这本书是<u>什么时候</u>借的？

> 谁
> 在哪儿
> 跟谁

(3) A: 你昨天买的那张地图，能不能借我用一下？

B: 行啊，到我房间去拿吧。

> 你在中国买
>
> 你朋友给你
>
> 我们昨天看过
>
> 上面有中文也有英文

第十一课

(4) A: 你吃了早饭打算干什么？

B: 吃了早饭，我要陪我爸妈去历史博物馆。

> 去商店买东西
>
> 去医院看病
>
> 去买飞机票

(5) A: 你们去了哪些地方？

B: 我们先去了香港，然后去了北京。

> 博物馆 …… 图书馆
>
> 长城 …… 故宫
>
> 一个学校 …… 一个公司

3. Fill in the blanks with the words given.

> 应该　　不错　　恐怕　　拿　　先　　会

(1) 你拍的照片都很_____。

(2) 你_____走吧，别等我。

(3) 书在桌子上，你自己_____吧。

(4) 过期不还的话，肯定_____有麻烦的。

(5) 已经十一点了，我想他_____不会来了。

(6) 要是你以后想做生意的话，你_____学经济。

4. Fill in the blanks with 了 or 的.

(1) A: 你知道吗？他父母亲来_____。

B: 是吗？什么时候来_____？

当代中文

A: 昨天。

B: 是坐飞机来_____吗？

A: 不，坐火车。

(2) A: 你昨天干什么_____？

B: 我去博物馆_____。

A: 你一个人去_____吗？

B: 不，跟我朋友一起去_____。

5. Sentence transformation.

E.g.

您养了一条很可爱的小狗。

→<u>您养的</u>小狗很可爱。

(1) 他去过很多地方。

→_____的地方很多。

(2) 他在北京拍了一些非常有意思的照片。

→_____的照片很有意思。

(3) 你是不是吃了不干净的东西？

→_____的东西是不是不干净？

(4) 昨天我们去了很远的地方。

→_____的地方很远。

6. Sentence expansion.

E.g.

这是书。

这是一本书。

这是一本新书。

这是一本很有意思的新书。

这是一本中国人写的新书。

这是一本中国人写的很有意思的新书。

(1) 这是照片。

这是＿＿＿＿＿＿＿＿＿照片。

这是＿＿＿＿＿＿＿＿＿＿＿＿照片。

这是＿＿＿＿＿＿＿＿＿＿＿＿＿＿＿照片。

这是＿＿＿＿＿＿＿＿＿＿＿＿＿＿＿＿＿＿照片。

(2) 朋友明天要来看我。

＿＿＿＿＿＿＿＿＿朋友明天要来看我。

＿＿＿＿＿＿＿＿＿＿＿＿朋友明天要来看我。

＿＿＿＿＿＿＿＿＿＿＿＿＿＿＿朋友明天要来看我。

＿＿＿＿＿＿＿＿＿＿＿＿＿＿＿＿＿＿朋友明天要来看我。

第十一课

7. Translate these sentences into Chinese.

(1) When did you come?

(2) —You haven't been to China before, have you?
   —Yes, I have.

(3) All of these are photos that I took in China.

(4) They are very interested in Chinese culture.

(5) Can you lend me the new map that you bought yesterday?

II. Listening comprehension

For each conversation, choose an appropriate answer for the second person after you have listened to what the first person says.

(1) A. 谢谢，我自己能行。

　　B. 你做什么生意？

　　C. 他是新来的。

(2) A. 不，去过。

　　B. 是的，去过。

　　C. 不，没去过。

(3) A. 我已经来了。

　　B. 是的，我在这儿。

　　C. 公司放假，我来旅行。

(4) A. 我是坐火车去的。

　　B. 上午去参观历史博物馆。

　　C. 今天下午陪我父母亲出去走走。

(5) A. 你可以先去。

　　B. 快要过期了。

　　C. 中国的经济。

(6) A. 太好了！现在能给我吗？

　　B. 对不起，我不知道你们的规定。

　　C. 这本书写得不错，你也应该看看。

(7) A. 那算了。

　　B. 别着急。

C. 这么厉害！

(8) A. 借给别人了。

B. 我不会骑。

C. 我自己用。

第十一课

III. Oral practice

1. Question and answer drill with your classmates.

(1) 你去哪儿旅行过？

(2) 你是什么时候去的？

(3) 你是怎么去的？

(4) 你是一个人去的还是跟朋友一起去的？

(5) 你拍照了吗？可以看一看你拍的照片吗？

(6) 这些照片是在哪儿拍的？

2. Tell your classmates about one of your travel experiences.

IV. Reading comprehension

Read the passage and answer the questions that follow.

马力从图书馆借了一本书，书名叫《怎么跟中国人做生意》。这本书是用英文写的，是一个美国人写的。马力说这本书不错，建议我也看看。他这本书是上个月二十号借的，快一个月了，所以得赶快去还，要是过了期的话，根据图书馆的规定，要罚款的。今天下午我们一起去图书馆，他去还书，我去借书。他要还的，我要借的，是同一本书，就是那本《怎么跟中国人做生意》。

Answer these questions.

1. 马力从图书馆借了一本什么书？是什么时候借的？

2. 这本书是谁写的？这本书怎么样？"我"看过吗？

3. 今天下午"我"跟马力去图书馆干什么？

V. Writing exercise

Write a short paragraph introducing the following book.

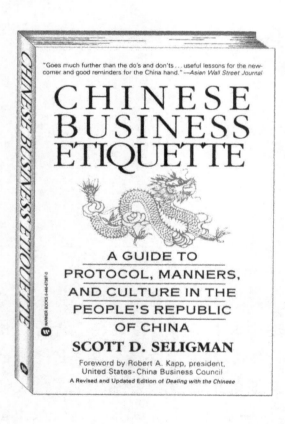

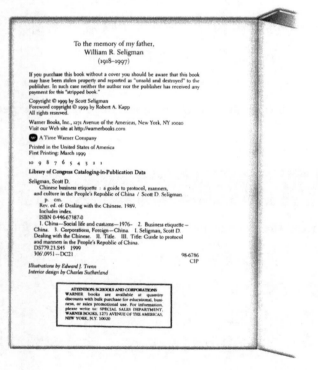

Supplementary words

建议	(N., V.)	jiànyì	suggestion, to suggest
根据	(Prep.)	gēnjù	according to
赶快	(Adv.)	gǎnkuài	quickly; hurry up
同	(Adj.)	tóng	same
介绍	(N., V.)	jièshào	introduction; to introduce
商贸	(N.)	shāngmào	business
礼节	(N.)	lǐjié	etiquette, courtesy, protocol
出版	(V.)	chūbǎn	to publish
出版社	(N.)	chūbǎnshè	publishing house

第十一课

当代中文

Dì-shí'èr Kè   Jīntiān Nǐ Chuān de zhēn Piàoliang

第十二课 今天你穿得真漂亮

Lesson 12   You're Dressed So Beautifully Today

I. Words and structures

1. Read aloud the following phrases.

前天	昨天	今天	明天	后天
前年	去年	今年	明年	后年

上个月   这个月   下个月

好听	好看	好吃	好玩儿
唱歌	唱一个歌	唱过歌	唱歌唱得很好听
跳舞	跳一个舞	跳过舞	跳舞跳得很优美
见面	见过面	见了面	跟他见一个面
问问题	回答问题	有问题	没有问题
很特别	特别的人	特别的事儿	特别好看
越来越好	越来越漂亮	越来越流利	越来越年轻

2. Substitution drills.

(1) 今天你<u>穿</u>得<u>真漂亮</u>。

来……真早
骑……特别快
吃……太少了

(2) 他的汉语说得<u>很好</u>。

比较流利	非常漂亮
很不错	不怎么样

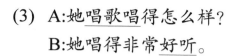

(3)　A:她<u>唱歌</u>唱得<u>怎么样</u>?
　　　B:她唱得非常<u>好听</u>。

打球 …… 打 …… 不错
跳舞 …… 跳 …… 优美
说汉语 …… 说 …… 流利
上课 …… 上 …… 有意思

第十二课

(4)　他越来越<u>漂亮</u>了。

老	忙
客气	喜欢她

(5)　他还想再<u>喝一杯</u>。

吃一点	买一件
借一本	唱一个
养一只	去一次

3. Fill in the blanks with the words given.

　　　属　　送　　祝　　见　　回答

(1)　老板让我明天下午去公司_____他。
(2)　我们应该_____他什么礼物呢?
(3)　_____你生日快乐!
(4)　我是1988年出生的,_____龙。
(5)　老师没有_____他的问题。

　　　得　　的

(6)　你汉语说_____很不错。
(7)　你_____汉语很不错。
(8)　你说汉语说_____很不错。
(9)　那个商店卖_____东西比较便宜。

4. Arrange the given words in the correct order to form a sentence.

(1)　他们　很　高兴　得　玩儿

当
代
中
文

(2) 我　睡　比较　晚　得　每天　都

(3) 生意　好　老板　高兴　越……越……　就

(4) 工作　做　多　得　钱　拿　多　得　越……越……　就

5. Translate these sentences into Chinese.

(1) You are dressed so beautifully today.

(2) She sings very well.

(3) Things are more and more expensive now.

(4) Happy birthday to you!

(5) This is my small gift for you.

II. Listening comprehension

Listen to each conversation, then choose an appropriate answer to each question.

(1) A. 前年　　　　　　　B. 去年　　　　　　　C. 今年

(2) A. 这个月　　　　　　B. 上个月　　　　　　C. 下个月

(3) A. 商店里的东西　　　B. 一张地图　　　　　C. 一次旅行活动

(4) A. 祝你快乐　　　　　B. 生日快乐　　　　　C. 新年快乐

(5) A. 认识　　　　　B. 不认识　　　　C. 很熟悉

(6) A. 24岁　　　　　B. 26岁　　　　　C. 20岁

(7) A. 她已经写得很快了　　B. 让男的别着急　　C. 别等她了

第十二课

III. Oral practice

Complete each dialogue according to the picture.

(1) A:你看，他正在起床。

　　B:他起得＿＿＿＿＿＿＿＿＿＿＿＿＿。

(2) A:你看，他正在吃早饭。

　　B:他吃得＿＿＿＿＿＿＿＿＿＿＿＿＿。

(3) A:他每天骑自行车去学校。

B:他骑得_____。

(4) A:你看，这是他做的功课。

B:他做得_____。

IV. Reading comprehension

Read the passage and answer the questions that follow.

张山是我的朋友。他高高的，胖胖的，每天睡得很早，起得很晚，吃得很多。他说他以前睡得很少，吃得很少，所以很瘦，现在吃得多了，睡得多了，所以就胖了。他平时穿得随随便便，一件T恤，一条短裤，可是去跟女朋友约会的时候，穿得特别漂亮。他爱骑自行车。每次都骑得特别快，快得让人害怕。他喜欢唱歌、跳舞，不过，他唱得不太好听，跳得不太优美。他不喝酒，因为他现在还不可以喝，明年就可以了。

Answer these questions.

1. 张山胖不胖？以前呢？

2. 他平时穿得怎么样？

3. 他骑自行车骑得怎么样？

4. 他唱歌唱得怎么样？跳舞跳得怎么样？

第十二课

V. Writing exercise

Write a short paragraph introducing someone you know, using the structure "V. 得 …".

Supplementary words

胖	(Adj.)	pàng	fat, chubby, plump
平时	(Adv.)	píngshí	normally, usually
随便	(Adj.)	suíbiàn	casual; doing as one pleases
T恤	(N.)	T-xù	T-shirt
短裤	(N.)	duǎnkù	shorts
害怕	(V.)	hàipà	to be afraid of, to be scared

Dì-shísān Kè　　Wǒ Jiāxiāng de Tiānqì Bǐ Zhèr Hǎo

第十三课　我家乡的天气比这儿好

Lesson 13　The Weather in My Hometown Is Better Than Here

I. Words and structures

1. Read aloud the following phrases.

一年四季　　春夏秋冬

春天/春季　夏天/夏季　　秋天/秋季　　冬天/冬季

冷　热　凉快　暖和　高　低　长　短

下雨　　　下大雨　　　下雪　　　下大雪　　　刮风　　刮大风

好极了　　快极了　　热极了　　美极了　　疼极了　有意思极了

麻烦极了　熟悉极了　新鲜极了　厉害极了　好听极了

这时候　　那时候　　什么时候　有的时候　最热的时候

2. Substitution drills.

(1) A:你家乡有没有这么<u>热</u>?
　　B:我家乡没有这么<u>热</u>。

冷　暖和　凉快
可爱　　漂亮

(2) A:你家乡有没有这么<u>热</u>?
　　B:我家乡跟这儿一样<u>热</u>。

冷　暖和　凉快
可爱　　漂亮

(3) A:你家乡的夏天有没有这么热?
　　B:我家乡的夏天比这儿<u>凉快多了</u>。

凉快得多
凉快一点儿
更热

当代中文

(4) A:夏天你常常去游泳吗？

B:<u>常常</u>去。

| 有时候 |
| 很少 |
| 从来不 |

(5) A:那儿的东西<u>贵</u>不<u>贵</u>?

B:一点儿也不<u>贵</u>。

| 多　便宜 |
| 好吃　新鲜 |

3. Fill in the blanks with the words given.

下　　刮　　来　　滑

(1) 冬天，我们常常到山上去＿＿＿＿＿雪。

(2) 天气预报说，明天要＿＿＿＿＿雨。

(3) 昨天晚上＿＿＿＿＿大风。

(4) 这儿的春天比我家乡＿＿＿＿＿得早。

大概　　　左右

(5) 今天＿＿＿＿＿有三十五度吧？

(6) 今天的最高温度是三十五度＿＿＿＿＿。

4. Make comparative sentences about the differences in the following chart.

（热　凉快　高　矮　大　小　胖　瘦　多　少）

今天：35℃	昨天：33℃
我们班：30个学生	你们班：25个学生
小张：25岁/178cm/100kg	小王：23岁/175cm/60kg

5. Translate these sentences into Chinese.

(1) It's very hot today.

(2) He is not as tall as you.

(3) It's much cooler in the summer in my hometown than here.

(4) This coat is the same size as that one.

(5) Which season do you like best?

第
十
三
课

II. Listening comprehension

Listen to each conversation, then choose an appropriate answer to each question.

(1) A. 52岁　　　　　　B. 55岁　　　　　　C. 58岁
(2) A. 春天和秋天　　　B. 夏天和冬天　　　C. 都不喜欢
(3) A. 跟这儿一样热　　B. 比这儿还热　　　C. 没有这儿热
(4) A. 太大了　　　　　B. 太小了　　　　　C. 不大不小
(5) A. 冬天　　　　　　B. 夏天　　　　　　C. 春天
(6) A. 晴天　　　　　　B. 多云　　　　　　C. 有雨
(7) A. 12℃　　　　　　B. 15℃　　　　　　C. 5℃

III. Oral practice

1. Compare two people or cities that you know.

2. How is the weather in your hometown? Describe it to your classmates.

IV. Reading comprehension

Read the passage and answer the questions that follow.

当代中文

　　上海跟北京一样，是中国最有名的两个大城市。上海人说，北京没有上海热闹；北京人说，上海没有北京漂亮。北京的面积比上海大得多，公园比上海多得多，历史比上海长得多；上海的人口比北京多一点儿，商店比北京漂亮一点儿。夏天，上海跟北京一样热，有的时候，北京比上海还热。冬天，上海没有北京那么冷，不过，上海人的家里一般没有暖气，北京人的家里家家都有暖气，所以，在上海工作、学习的北京人常常说，上海比北京更冷。

Answer these questions.

　　1. 北京大还是上海大？

　　2. 夏天北京比上海凉快一点儿，是不是？

　　3. 冬天北京冷还是上海冷？

V. Writing exercise

Write a short paragraph comparing two people or two cities that you know.

第
十
三
课

Supplementary words

矮	(Adj.)	ǎi	short (of height)
高	(Adj.)	gāo	tall
重	(Adj.)	zhòng	heavy
有名	(Adj.)	yǒumíng	famous
面积	(N.)	miànjī	area
公园	(N.)	gōngyuán	park
人口	(N.)	rénkǒu	population
一般	(Adv., Adj.)	yìbān	generally speaking; general

Dì-shísì Kè   Wǒ Lǎojiā Zài Dōngběi
第十四课 我老家在东北
Lesson 14   My Hometown Is in the Northeast

I. Words and structures

1. Read aloud the following phrases.

海边　　河边　　路边　　门边

早饭　　中饭/午饭　　晚饭

东北　　东南　　西北　　西南

热死了　吵死了　高兴死了

楼上　　楼下　　上楼　　下楼　　大楼　　高楼　　小楼

宿舍东边　商店南边　学校西边　我家北边　教室对面

2. Substitution drills.

(1) 我家北边是<u>山</u>，南边是<u>河</u>。

| 海 …… 山 |
| 邮局 …… 银行 |
| 公园 …… 停车场 |

(2) 那儿<u>一定</u>很热闹。

| 大概　肯定 |
| 可能　不一定 |
| 不可能 |

(3) A: 你家离<u>海</u>远吗？

B: 不太远，开车去的话，大概需要半个小时。

> 学校　　市中心
> 你工作的地方

(4) A: 你去学校的餐厅吃饭吗？

B: 我<u>有时候</u>去。

> 从来不
> 很少　　常常

(5) A: 吃完晚饭，你干什么？

B: 吃完晚饭，我就去<u>海边散步</u>。

> 看看电视
> 出去走走
> 喝一杯茶

第十四课

3. Fill in the blanks with the words given.

新鲜　　优美　　方便　　热闹

(1) 农村空气_____，环境_____。

(2) 他的老家有很多山，所以交通不太_____。

(3) 我家在市中心，从早到晚，车水马龙，_____极了。

离　　从　　往　　到　　给　　对

(4) 我家_____学校不太远。

(5) _____我家到学校不太远。

(6) 你打算_____哪儿去？

(7) 明天晚上我_____你打电话。

(8) 他_____我们非常客气。

(9) 到十字路口，_____右拐，就是我家。

4. Arrange the given words in the correct order to form a sentence.

(1) 小楼后面　　　一个车库　　　是

当代中文

(2) 西部　　美国　　我家　　在

(3) 树　　花儿　　和　　很多　　院子里　　有

(4) 现在　　可能　　在　　还　　睡觉　　他

(5) 他　　客气　　很　　我们　　对

5. Translate these sentences into Chinese.

(1) There's a mountain to the north of my home and there's a river to the south.

(2) Is your home far from the sea?

(3) There are shops to the east and west of my home, and many restaurants too.

(4) I drive to school every day. It takes me about half an hour.

(5) This gift was bought for you.

II. Listening comprehension

Listen to each conversation, then choose an appropriate answer to each question.

(1) A. 吃晚饭以前　　　B. 吃早饭以前　　　C. 吃晚饭以后

(2) A. 大商店的西边　　B. 大商店的东边　　C. 银行的东边

(3) A. 很喜欢　　　　　B. 比较喜欢　　　　C. 不喜欢

(4) A. 开车去　　　　　B. 坐车去　　　　　C. 骑车去

(5) A. 很热闹   B. 有山有水   C. 交通不方便

(6) A. 昨天晚上喝了很多酒

    B. 昨天晚上没有休息好

    C. 昨天晚上来了很多朋友

(7) A. 男的以前养过一只狗

    B. 男的现在的家没有院子

    C. 男的不知道养什么花儿比较好

第十四课

III.   Oral practice

1. Question and answer drill with your classmates.

(1) 你家在城市还是在农村?

(2) 那儿热闹吗?

(3) 你家离学校远不远?

(4) 你每天怎么来学校? 大概需要多少时间?

2. Describe the surroundings of your house.

IV.   Reading comprehension

Read the passage and answer the questions that follow.

> 我家在市区, 那儿很热闹。我家北面是商店, 东面有一个医院, 西面和南面都是住宅。我家附近还有一个大超市。公共汽车站和地铁站离我家也不远。我每天坐地铁上班, 只要半个小时。所以, 买东西、上班都很方便。可是, 最大的问题是, 我家在马路旁边, 从早到晚, 车水马龙, 吵得我不能休息。我们下个月就要搬家了。新家比较远, 在郊区, 不过没关系, 我刚买了汽车。以后欢迎你去我家玩儿, 我开车带你去。

Answer these questions.

    1. 他家在市区还是郊区？

    2. 那儿交通方便不方便？

    3. 他喜欢现在住的地方吗？

    4. 他现在怎么上下班？搬了家以后呢？

当代中文

V. Writing exercise

Write a short paragraph describing the surroundings of your house.

Supplementary words

公园	(N.)	gōngyuán	park
停车场	(N.)	tíngchēchǎng	parking area
市区	(N.)	shìqū	urban district
郊区	(N.)	jiāoqū	suburban district

住宅	(N.)	zhùzhái	residence
超市	(N.)	chāoshì	supermarket
上班	(V.O.)	shàngbān	to go to work
搬家	(V.O.)	bān jiā	to move house
带	(V.)	dài	to take, carry

第十四课

当代中文

Dì-shíwǔ Kè   Wǒ Xuéguo Bàn Nián Hànyǔ

第十五课　我学过半年汉语

Lesson 15　I Have Studied Chinese for Half a Year

I.　Words and structures

1.　Read aloud the following phrases.

一年	一天	一个月	一个星期	一个小时
半年	半天	半个月	半个星期	半个小时
一年半	一天半	一个半月	一个半星期	一个半小时

再说一遍　　再写一遍　　再听一遍　　再看一遍

说得很流利　说得很标准　说得很清楚　说得很慢

早就学过了　已经学过了　刚刚学过　　还没学过

2.　Substitution drills.

(1) 您说得太快了，请您说得慢一点儿。

写 ……	小 ……	大
坐 ……	远 ……	近
开 ……	慢 ……	快

(2) 我的汉语口语还可以，听力不行。

阅读 ……	写作
发音 ……	语法

(3) A: 你学了多长时间(汉语）了？
　　B: 我学了两年(汉语）了。

半年	两年
六个月	

(4) A: 你们一个星期见几次面?
　　B: 我们一个星期见三次面。

打 …… 球
上 …… 汉语课
去 …… 图书馆

听　看　写

第十五课

(5) A: 请你再说一遍。
　　B: 好，我再说一遍。

3. **Translate these expressions into Chinese.**

a year	three days
a month	two weeks
a year and a half	half a day
two months and a half	half a week
half an hour	25 minutes

4. **Place the given words in the correct place within each sentence.**

(1) 我跟他A见过B面C。(一次)
(2) 我A学过B汉语C。(半年)
(3) 我每天A看B电视C。(一个小时)
(4) 我A在他家吃过B饭C。(三次)
(5) 我A听了B录音C，可还是不明白。(两遍)

5. **Translate these sentences into Chinese.**

(1) How long have you been studying Chinese?

(2) Would you please say it again?

当代中文

(3) The test yesterday was not difficult.

(4) Would you please speak a bit more slowly?

(5) I have been there many times.

II. Listening comprehension

Listen to each conversation, then choose an appropriate answer to each question.

(1) A. 听力不太好　　　B. 口语不太好　　　C. 阅读不太好

(2) A. 汉语　　　　　　B. 英语　　　　　　C. 汉语和英语

(3) A. 发音　　　　　　B. 汉字　　　　　　C. 语法

(4) A. 很好　　　　　　B. 不好　　　　　　C. 他自己也不知道

(5) A. 英语　　　　　　B. 中文　　　　　　C. 经济

(6) A. 忘了他自己的房间号码

　　　B. 想知道朋友的房间号码

　　　C. 想要给马丁打一个电话

(7) A. 男的对这儿不熟悉

　　　B. 男的在这儿没生过病

　　　C. 男的到这儿以后去过一次医院

III. Oral practice

1. Question and answer drill with your classmates.

(1) 你学了多长时间汉语了？

(2) 你每个星期学习几个小时汉语？

(3) 你去过中国吗？去过几次？

(4) 你听不听课文的录音？听几遍？

2. Give a talk answering these questions: What do you think about learning Mandarin Chinese? What are the easiest and the most difficult aspects of it? Why?

IV. Reading comprehension

Read the passage and answer the questions that follow.

你好！你能说一口标准的汉语普通话吗？你想提高你的英语听说水平吗？那么，跟我交朋友吧！

我叫江山，男，大学三年级学生，母语是英语。我学了半年多汉语了，能说一些简单的汉语，但是说得很不流利。我希望找一个能说标准普通话的中国人，练习汉语听力和口语。我们可以用一半时间说汉语，一半时间说英语。我每天晚上都有空，周末也可以见面。如果你有兴趣，请给我打电话。我的电话号码是：1234567。

第十五课

Answer these questions.

1. 江山的母语是什么？

2. 他要找一个怎么样的中国人？

3. 他学了多长时间汉语了？

V. Writing exercise

Write a short paragraph about your experiences in studying Chinese.

当代中文

Supplementary words

发音	(N.)	fāyīn	pronunciation
语法	(N.)	yǔfǎ	grammar
录音	(N., V.O.)	lùyīn	recording; to record
提高	(V.)	tígāo	to raise
水平	(N.)	shuǐpíng	level
简单	(Adj.)	jiǎndān	simple
希望	(N., V.)	xīwàng	(to) hope
周末	(N.)	zhōumò	weekend

Dì-shíliù Kè   Huǒchēpiào Mài-wán le

第十六课　火车票卖完了

Lesson 16   The Train Tickets Have Been Sold Out

I. Words and structures

1. Read aloud the following phrases.

说错	写错	买错	打错			
用坏	穿坏	吃坏	办坏			
买到	看到	见到	谈到(十一点)	开到(宿舍门口)		
说完	卖完	学完	干完	做完	吃完	喝完
摔倒	摔伤	摔坏	摔破	摔死		
写好	写完	写错	写对	写清楚		

2. Substitution drills.

(1) 他骑得很快，右手还拿着东西。

鲜花
一件礼物
一个蛋糕

(2) 他在北京工作的时候，拍了很多照片。

我登长城
他们一起旅行
我们在海边散步

(3) <u>买到车票</u>以后请您给我们发一个传真。

> 谈好生意
> 看完市场
> 安排好活动

(4) A: <u>星期二的火车票</u>还有吗?
B: <u>星期二的火车票</u>已经卖完了。

> 汉英词典
> 《当代中文》
> 下星期一的飞机票

(5) A: 您下星期二到没问题吧?
B: <u>看来</u>不行了,要推迟到星期三。

> 恐怕　大概　可能

3. **Fill in the blanks with the words given.**

　　安排　　打算　　参加　　参观　　发生

(1) 昨天的晚会你_____了没有?

(2) 欢迎你们来_____我们公司。

(3) 前面是不是_____了交通事故?

(4) 上完大学以后,你_____做什么工作?

(5) 我有个朋友想去贵校学习,能不能给他_____一个房间?

(6) 你明天有什么_____?

　　倒　　伤　　坏　　破　　疼

(7) 昨天晚上刮大风,刮_____了很多大树。

(8) 这本词典_____了,能不能换一本?

(9) 我的汽车_____了,我要请人修一下。

(10) 她的话_____了我的心。

(11) 我肚子有点儿_____。

4. **Complete the sentences using the expressions from Exercise 1.**

(1) A: 昨天晚上你们谈了很长时间吧?

B: 没有。我们_____九点就休息了。

(2) A: 你上午去书店了?

B: 是啊, 我想买一本汉英词典。可是汉英词典卖完了, 我没_____。

(3) A: 这两个句子我写得对不对?

B: 有两个汉字你_____了, 别的都对。

(4) A: 喂, 王海在家吗?

B: 这儿没有王海, 你_____了。

(5) A: 你怎么啦?

B: 我肚子疼。

A: 你是不是吃了不新鲜的东西, _____了肚子?

(6) A: 路上有雪, 小心别_____。

B: 放心吧。

第十六课

5. **Complete these sentences using "V.着 ...".**

(1) 你看: 他_____眼镜, _____红衬衫, 手里_____花儿。

(2) 老师在教室里站着，同学们都_____。

(3) 房间的门_____，我进去一看，里面没人。

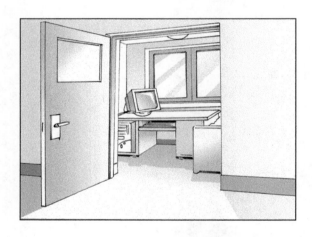

6. **Translate these sentences into Chinese.**

(1) The train tickets for Tuesday have sold out.

(2) Please send us a fax when you get the ticket, to inform us of your flight number.

(3) Didn't you see her crossing the road when you were riding?

(4) He rode very quickly, holding something in his right hand.

(5) When can we finish this textbook?

II. Listening comprehension

For each conversation, choose an appropriate answer for the second person after you have listened to what the first person says.

(1) A. 我想问一个问题。

　　B. 是吗？那好极了！

　　C. 没问题，我认识路。

(2) A. 行，再见！

　　B. 好，那样吧。

　　C. 您说吧。

(3) A. 不会是汽车。

　　B. 可能坏了吧。

　　C. 骑得太快了。

(4) A. 有些什么活动？

　　B. 好，请你安排一下。

　　C. 那我们马上就开始吧。

(5) A. 11点半。

　　B. CA901。

　　C. 900块。

(6) A. 我忘了号码。

　　B. 我没看清楚。

　　C. 汽车上没有水。

(7) A. 自行车没摔坏。

　　B. 我打着雨伞。

　　C. 背上有点儿疼。

III. Oral practice

Describe what is depicted in each picture.

当代中文

IV. Reading comprehension

This is a page from a train schedule. Answer the questions below, according to this schedule.

长春⇌上海

1348/5 长春→上海 普快	自上海起公里	站 名	1346/7 上海→长春 普快
16:19	2356	长春	— 15:42
59 17:03	2294	公主岭	56 52
44 48	2240	四平	17 14:13
18:28 32	2187	昌图	25 13:22
19:13 17	2122	铁岭	40 12:37
20:07 17	2057	沈阳北	56 11:48
21:46 50	1957	大虎山	07 10:04
22:54 58	1812	锦州	9:01 57
23:32 49	1761	葫芦岛	22 19
0:05 09	1740	兴城	03 8:00
1:27 35	1628	上海关	51 6:43
49 53	1612	秦皇岛	23 19
2:10 13	1590	北戴河	6:02 59
	1562	昌黎	38 5:35
3:02 05	1524	滦县	
4:02 06	1449	唐山	16 4:12
5:36 44	1326	天津	42 2:34
8:19 25	1087	德州	0:00 23:54
9:55 10:07	966	济南	14 22:02
11:05 09	895	泰山	06 21:02
12:07 13	810	兖州	08 20:02
14:01 11	649	徐州	15 18:06
15:09 13	574	宿州	09 17:05
16:14 22	484	蚌埠	58 15:49
18:34 48	303	南京	37 13:25
19:32 36	238	镇江	39 35
54 58	209	丹阳	17 12:04
20:34 42	165	常州	34 11:28
21:10 15	126	无锡	57 50
41 49	84	苏州	24 10:05
22:14 17	48	昆山	41 38
22:48 —	0	上海	9:08

大连⇌上海

T131/4 大连→上海 特快	自大连起公里	站 名	T132/3 上海→大连 特快
11:57	0	大连	— 15:56
13:04 07	105	瓦房店	44 14:39
14:28 34	240	大石桥	23 13:20
15:38 40	380	盘锦	12 12:10
16:41 43	443	锦州	05 11:03
18:41 49	627	山海关	15 9:07
19:03 05	643	秦皇岛	
20:48 50	806	唐山	
22:14 22	929	天津	53 5:45
	1054	沧州	23 4:21
	1168	德州	18 3:16
1:50 58	1289	济南	59 1:51
2:46 48	1360	泰山	
5:13 15	1606	徐州	36 22:34
6:56 7:04	1771	蚌埠	21:03 20:55
8:51 56	1952	南京	09 19:04
9:31 34	2017	镇江	26 18:23
10:16 19	2090	常州	43 40
43 46	2129	无锡	16 17:12
11:08 11	2171	苏州	50 47
11:57 —	2255	上海	16:03

当代中文

Answer these questions.

1. 从上海到长春的火车几点钟开车？车次是多少？从上海到长春需要多长时间？

2. 从上海到大连的火车几点钟开车？车次是多少？从上海到大连需要多长时间？

3. 从上海去南京，可以坐几点的火车？什么时候到南京？

V. Writing exercise

Beike was originally planning to go to Datong（大同）city on Tuesday, but he wasn't able to get a train ticket, so he had to postpone his trip to Wednesday. He has now bought a train ticket for Wednesday. The train number is T23, and the arrival time is Wednesday, 3:15 p.m. Write a fax message to Xiao Huang, Beike's friend in Datong, to inform him of the reason for the change in itinerary and to ask him to pick Beike up from the station on time.

Supplementary words

别的	（Pron.）	biéde	other
小心	（Adj.）	xiǎoxīn	careful
车次	（N.）	chēcì	train number

第十七课 现在就可以搬进去

Dì-shíqī Kè   Xiànzài Jiù Kěyǐ Bān-jìnqu

Lesson 17   You Can Move In Right Now

第十七课

I. Words and structures

1. Read aloud the following phrases.

有办法	没办法	好办法	什么办法
坐电梯	坐地铁	坐飞机	坐火车
付钱	付租金	付押金	付学费(fèi, fee)
很生气	不生气	别生气	生谁的气
带来	带去	送来	送去
拆下来	装上去	搬进来	搬出去

拿来   拿去   拿出来 拿出去 拿回来 拿回去

走进   走出   走上   走下   走进去   走出去 走上去

走进房间来   走出教室去   走上楼去   拿回家来

2. Substitution drills.

(1) 如果你们想租的话，现在就可以搬进去。

参加 …… 报名
换钱 …… 去银行
滑雪 …… 去

(2) 每天走上走下，太累了。

搬上搬下
骑来骑去
拿进拿出

当代中文

(3) 这<u>合同</u>我们可以带回去看看吗?

> 地图　课本　广告

(4) 要不要<u>上楼去</u>看看?

> 进房间去
> 回家去
> 走出校门去

(5) 我<u>一</u>有空<u>就</u>去买。

> 下课 …… 回家
> 高兴 …… 唱歌
> 去人多的地方 …… 头疼

3. Fill in the blanks with the words given.

　　　租　　锻炼　　练习　　送　　发

(1) 他每天起床以后第一件事就是_____身体。

(2) 他每天晚上用一个小时_____汉字。

(3) 他有两套房子,一套_____给别人,一套自己住。

(4) 他在学校附近_____了一个公寓,这样,住得比较舒服,去学校也比较方便。

(5) 请你_____一个传真给他,告诉他我们的航班,请他去接我们。

(6) 您放心,您买的电视机今天下午就给您_____过去。

4. Fill in the blanks using these directional verbs as the complements.

　　　来　　去　　出来　　上……去　　出……去

(1) 下课了,同学们一个个都走_____教室_____。

(2) 我朋友从北京带_____了一些中国的工艺品。

(3) 昨天我们去医院看一位朋友,给他带_____了一束鲜花。

(4) 他从房间里搬_____一台电视机,放在门外面。

(5) 他住在二十楼,今天电梯坏了,他只好走_____楼_____。

5. Complete these sentences.

(1) 我一有空就_____。

(2) 我一上完课就_____。

(3) 他一回来就_____。

(4) 他一回来，我就_____。

(5) 一放假，我们就_____。

6. Translate these sentences into Chinese.

    (1) If you want to rent it, you can move in right now.

    (2) It's very tiring to walk upstairs and downstairs every day.

    (3) Can we take this contract home to read?

    (4) I will send you a fax as soon as I have bought the ticket.

    (5) The technician said the air conditioner is too old to be fixed.

第十七课

II. Listening comprehension

Listen to each conversation, then choose an appropriate answer to each question.

(1) A. 一个月以后   B. 一个星期以后   C. 不可能修好了

(2) A. 有电视机，没有洗衣机

    B. 有洗衣机，没有电视机

    C. 没有电视机，也没有洗衣机

(3) A. 跟师傅学   B. 在学校学   C. 在家自学

(4) A. 女的想要租一套房子

    B. 江河清是这里的房东

    C. 男的上个月刚搬进来

当代中文

(5) A. 空调公司　　　　　B. 电话公司　　　　　C. 食品商店

(6) A. 昨天上午402家里没人

　　 B. 女的很可能住在四楼

　　 C. 男的昨天去了702室

(7) A. 有人撞倒了她

　　 B. 撞她的人没有说"对不起"

　　 C. 撞她的人没有陪她去医院检查

III.　Oral practice

Read the advertisments and choose an apartment that seems satisfactory to you; then call the rental agency to ask for more detailed information.

IV.　Reading comprehension

Read the passage and answer the questions that follow.

王英和张园园一起租了一套公寓。这套公寓有两个卧室，一个客厅，一个卫生间，一个厨房。家具、电器都有。一个月租金两千五百块。她们比较满意。可是，搬进去没几天，空调就坏了。这么热的天，没有空调怎么行？她们很生气，给房东打了好几个电话。昨天，房东给她们送来了一台新空调。装上新空调，她们刚开始高兴了两个小时，麻烦又来了：电话机出了问题，别人可以打进来，她们不能打出去。这更麻烦了：她们只好走出房间去给房东打公用电话了。

第十七课

Answer these questions.

(1) 王英和张园园住的公寓每个月房租多少？

(2) 空调是什么时候坏的？

(3) 现在又出了什么问题？

V. Writing exercise

You are renting an apartment with a living room and two bedrooms, complete with appliances, for a monthly cost of 2,000 yuan. It is quite near to the school; about a ten-minute bike ride. Now you want to find a roommate to share the rent with you. Write a notice to be posted on the school bulletin board. In the notice, include a description of yourself, the general condition of the apartment you are renting, and your request for a roommate.

Supplementary words

广告	(N.)	guǎnggào	advertisement
工艺品	(N.)	gōngyìpǐn	handicraft article
束	(M.W.)	shù	a bunch of
卧室	(N.)	wòshì	bedroom
客厅	(N.)	kètīng	sitting room, parlour
家具	(N.)	jiājù	furniture
满意	(Adj.)	mǎnyì	satisfactory
又	(Adv.)	yòu	again
公用电话		gōngyòng diànhuà	public telephone

Dì-shíbā Kè Wǒ Kǒngpà Tīng-bu-dǒng

第十八课　我 恐怕 听不懂

Lesson 18　I'm Afraid I Won't Understand

第
十
八
课

I. Words and structures

1. Read aloud the following phrases.

下了一场大雨	看了一场电影	演了一场京剧
慢慢地走过来	高兴地告诉他	安安静静地休息一会儿
连一分钱也没有	连小孩子也知道	
忙得连饭也没时间吃	累得连话也不想说	
听得清楚　听不清楚	看得懂	看不懂
吃得完　吃不完	赶得到	赶不到
骑得动　骑不动	买得到	买不到
起得来　起不来	进得去	进不去
爬得上去　爬不上去	开得进去	开不进去

2. Substitution drills.

(1) 我恐怕<u>听不懂</u>吧。

看不懂
学不会
做不完

(2) A: <u>票</u> <u>买得到</u>吗?
  B: 肯定<u>买得到</u>。

房子……租
朋友……找
中国菜……吃

(3) A: 我爬不动了。

B: 咱们休息休息吧。

走　骑　跑

(4) A: 半个小时赶得到吗?

B: 恐怕赶不到。

十分钟
一刻钟
一个小时

(5) 他累得连话都说不出来了。

饭……不想吃
路……走不动

3. **Fill in the blanks with the words given.**

注意　　建议　　教　　跑　　爬　　赶

(1) 请_____"参"这个字的发音,是cān,不是kān。

(2) 他们有两位汉语老师,一位_____读写,一位_____听说。

(3) 你这么着急,是要去_____几点的飞机?

(4) 小时侯,他喜欢_____树;大了以后,他喜欢_____山。

(5) 每天早上,我们都能看到他在校园里_____步。

的　　地　　得

(6) 这是我养_____花儿。

(7) 他做_____菜很好吃。

(8) 他菜做_____很好吃。

(9) 看,那位老人慢慢_____走过来了。

(10) 他走_____很慢。

4. **Complete the sentence with the appropriate expression.**

(1) 老师,黑板上的字太小了,我_____。

A. 不能看清楚　　　　B. 看不清楚　　　C. 看得不清楚

(2) 我到电影院的时候,电影票已经卖完了,我_____。

A. 买不到　　　　　　B. 没买到　　　　C. 不买到

(3) 这是我的房间，可是我忘了带钥匙，_____。

    A. 不能进去   B. 不可以进去   C. 进不去

(4) 你今天_____，有什么重要的活动？

    A. 穿得这么漂亮   B. 穿得漂亮   C. 穿漂亮了

5. Translate these sentences into Chinese.

(1) You may not be able to understand just by listening, but you can surely understand by watching.

(2) It seems that I cannot get to the top of the mountain.

(3) It is said in the newspaper that they are all very famous.

(4) It's not that you don't have time to exercise; it's that you are lazy, I'm afraid.

(5) This question is so easy. Even a child could answer it.

第十八课

II. Listening comprehension

Listen to the conversations, then choose an appropriate answer to each question.

(1) A. 有一张   B. 有很多   C. 没有

(2) A. 开汽车去   B. 骑自行车去   C. 走着去

(3) A. 他太太来了   B. 他非常懒   C. 他不应该在家里

(4) A. 工作太忙了   B. 学习太累了   C. 环境太差了

(5) A. 马丁比江山更熟悉中国

    B. 江山比马丁更熟悉中国

    C. 马丁跟江山一样，都不熟悉中国

(6) A. 打球　　　　　B. 爬山　　　　　C. 跑步
(7) A. 在出租车上　　B. 在地铁车站　　C. 在飞机上

III. Oral practice

Question and answer drill with your classmates.

你常常运动吗？你喜欢什么运动？

IV. Reading comprehension

Read the passage and answer the questions that follow.

那天，我去电影院看一部外国电影。我一进去，电影就开始了。过了一会儿，进来了一男一女，他们在我前面的座位上坐下，然后就开始不停地说话。电影里的谈话我一点儿也听不见。我很生气，对他们说："你们怎么回事？我一点儿都听不见了！"他们回头看看我，对我说："我们这是私人谈话，你不用听！"我说："我是说，我听不见电影里的话，不是听不见你们的话！"他们笑了，说："电影里说的都是外国话，我们听不懂，听它干什么！"

Answer these questions.

(1) "我" 为什么听不见电影里的谈话？
(2) 电影里说的外语 "我" 听得懂吗？
(3) 坐在我前面的那两个人听得懂吗？

V. Writing exercise

Write a short paragraph based on the dialogue in text 2, with the words given.

李小雨、田中、马力、高一飞一起……，……的时候，李小雨……了，所以，她决定让……，她自己……。马力觉得……，王英希望她……，田中建议她……，高一飞打算……。但是，李小雨现在最需要的是……。

第十八课

Supplementary words

钥匙	(N.)	yàoshi	key
校园	(N.)	xiàoyuán	campus
部	(M.W.)	bù	measure word (for a movie)
停	(V.)	tíng	to stop
私人	(Adj.)	sīrén	private
对……说		duì...shuō	to say to someone

当代中文

Dì-shíjiǔ Kè　　Wǒ　Bǎ　Qiánbāo Wàng-zài Chē shang le

第 十 九 课　 我 把 钱 包 忘 在 车 上 了

Lesson 19　 I've Left My Wallet in the Car

I.　Words and structures

1.　Read aloud the following phrases.

在汽车上　　在火车上　　在飞机上

赶快来　　　赶快走　　　赶快出发

东西丢了　　钱包丢了　　发票丢了

开一张发票　　要一张发票　　拿一张发票

觉得有点儿冷　　觉得很不错　　觉得他不像话

扔一个球　　扔过来　　扔给我　　扔到垃圾箱里

交房租　　交上来　　交上去　　交给谁　　交到哪儿去

放书　　放下　　放进去　　放在床上　　放在口袋里

2.　Substitution drills.

(1) 我<u>马上</u>把钱包给你们送过来。

明天	肯定
不可能	

(2) A: 你把<u>钱包</u>放在哪儿了？
　　B: 我把<u>钱包</u>放在包里了。

礼物	衣服	照片

(3) A: 你把它扔到哪儿去了？
　　B: 我把它扔到<u>垃圾箱里</u>去了。

河里	床下
门外面	

(4) A: 你买的花儿真漂亮！

B: 我要把它送给<u>我的女朋友</u>。

我的父母亲
我的老师
我的太太

(5) A: 你还记得<u>车号</u>吗？

B: 我一点儿也想不起来了。

他的地址
他说的那句话
我们三年前在上海见过的那个老人

第十九课

3. **Fill in the blanks with the words given.**

记　　记住　　记得

(1) 你还_____我吗？我们去年见过一面。

(2) 朋友们的电话号码，他都_____在心里。

(3) 他只听我说一遍就_____了。

刚　　刚才

(4) 你_____去哪儿了？

(5) 我_____到这儿，对附近还不熟悉。

(6) _____我在他家吃饭的时候，发现他家的人都爱吃甜食。

张　　本　　顿　　遍

(7) 他一天只吃两_____：早饭和晚饭，不吃午饭。

(8) 这_____护照上的照片看上去不像你。

(9) 他把宾馆的地址写在一_____纸上。

(10) 他的听力真糟糕，我说了三_____他才明白。

4. **Complete these sentences.**

(1) 他买了一束漂亮的花儿，打算把花儿_____。

(2) 我住在六楼。我让他们把空调送到家里，可是师傅把空调_____就走了，我得自己把空调搬上楼去。真不像话！

(3) 别人都把冰箱放在厨房里，可他把冰箱_____，真奇怪！

(4) 这里不能停汽车，请你把汽车_____。

5. Translate these sentences into Chinese.

(1) I put the wallet on the seat.

(2) I left my wallet in the car.

(3) He rented the room to a foreigner.

(4) Let's move this washing machine to the bathroom.

(5) When we got out of the car just now, I was the one who paid the money.

II. Listening comprehension

Listen to the conversations, then choose an appropriate answer to each question.

(1) A. 她忘了那个人的名字

　　 B. 她不想知道那个人的名字

　　 C. 她还要想一想

(2) A. 宾馆　　　　　　 B. 商店　　　　　　 C. 学校

(3) A. 钱包里　　　　　 B. 旅行包里　　　　 C. 口袋里

(4) A. 他没有证件　　　 B. 他不是学生　　　 C. 他没带借书证

(5) A. 桌子上　　　　　 B. 床上　　　　　　 C. 垃圾箱里

(6) A. 很客气　　　　　 B. 不诚实　　　　　 C. 记不住事儿

(7) A. 男的对自己的生日不感兴趣

　　 B. 女的记错了她爱人的生日

　　 C. 女的忘了买生日蛋糕

第
十
九
课

III. Oral practice

1. Question and answer drill with your classmates.

你丢过东西吗？怎么丢的？后来找到了没有？

2. Wei Lian left his wallet in the taxi again. However, he didn't throw the receipt into the garbage this time. Here is the receipt. The taxi company's telephone number is on it. Wei Lian's Chinese is not very good; can you call the taxi company for him?

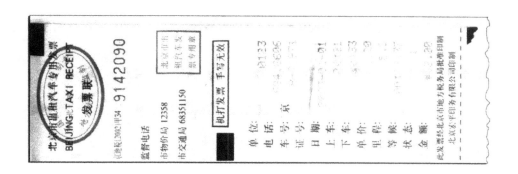

IV. Reading comprehension

Read the passage and answer the questions that follow.

　　老王师傅开了十几年车，第一次见到这么糊涂的老外：把钱包忘在了出租汽车的座位上。不过，发现钱包的不是老王，是一位乘客。乘客把钱包交给老王，老王就把钱包交给了公司领导。领导打开钱包一看，里面有五百美元，还有一张信用卡，其他什么也没有。领导也没办法了，没有名字，没有地址，到哪儿去找？可是，老王不着急：发票上有公司的电话号码，那位老外发现丢了钱包，一定会打电话来的。那就等着吧。等了三天，打来电话的真不少，有忘了雨伞的，有忘了行李的，可就是没有忘了钱包的。老王觉得奇怪了：怎么，那位老外一直到现在还不知道自己丢了钱包？

Answer these questions.

(1) 发现钱包以后，老王把它交给了谁？

(2) 钱包里有些什么？

(3) 老王为什么不着急？

(4) 丢钱包的人打来过电话吗？

当代中文

V. Writing exercise

Yesterday at dinnertime, you left a bag in the school's dining hall. There were a few books and some money in the bag. You hope that whoever finds the bag will return it to you, so you write a notice to be posted on the school's bulletin board. The notice should include the time and place you lost your bag, the contents of the bag, and how to contact you.

第十九课

Supplementary words

束	(M.W.)	shù	a bunch of
甜食	(N.)	tiánshí	sweet food, dessert
奇怪	(Adj.)	qíguài	strange, confusing
停	(V.)	tíng	to stop, to park (a vehicle)
信用卡	(N.)	xìnyòngkǎ	credit card
行李	(N.)	xíngli	luggage
桌子	(N.)	zhuōzi	desk, table
记性	(N.)	jìxing	memory

Dì-èrshí Kè   Chà Diǎnr Bèi Qìchē Zhuàngle Yíxià
第二十课　差点儿被汽车　撞了一下
Lesson 20　I Was Nearly Knocked Down by a Car

I. Words and structures

1. Read aloud the following phrases.

寄一封信　　寄给谁　　寄到哪儿去

糟透了　　　坏透了　　忙透了

东西掉了　　掉下来　　掉在地上

吃掉　　卖掉　　送掉　　砍掉　　烧掉

变大了　　变老了　　变瘦了　　变漂亮了　变得我不认识了

又来了　　又下雨了　又工作了　又干净了　又可以了

2. Substitution drills.

(1) 我等了<u>一个多小时</u>才<u>拿到钱</u>。

| 半个多小时 …… 买到票 |
| 五个小时 …… 上飞机 |
| 半天 …… 见到他 |

(2) 刚才我差点儿<u>让</u>汽车撞了一下。

| 叫 | 被 |

(3) 路两边的树都被<u>砍</u>倒了。

| 刮 | 撞 |

(4) 河里的鱼都被毒死了。

院子里的花儿
天上的鸟
家里的狗

（5）A:你的自行车呢？
　　B:我的自行车叫人偷走了。

借　　骑　　搬

第二十课

3. **Fill in the blanks with the words given.**

变　　　换

（1）一美元＿＿＿＿＿＿多少人民币？
（2）天气＿＿＿＿＿＿得越来越热了。

寄　　打　　发

（3）你＿＿＿＿＿＿给我的信，我收到了。
（4）刚才我接到一个电话，是一个不认识的人＿＿＿＿＿＿来的。
（5）他＿＿＿＿＿＿给我们的电子邮件有病毒，别打开。

4. **Choose the correct sentence.**

（1）A. 他把汽车撞了一下，差点儿撞死。
　　B. 他被汽车撞了一下，差点儿撞死。
（2）A. 今天的票卖完了，你明天再来买吧。
　　B. 今天的票被卖完了，你明天再来买吧。
（3）A. 这本书你看过吗？
　　B. 这本书被你看过吗？
（4）A. 刚才小王被小李打了一顿。
　　B. 刚才小王小李打了一顿。

5. **Translate these sentences into Chinese.**

（1）The bicycle was stolen by somebody.

当代中文

(2) There was something wrong with the computer.

(3) I was riding too fast to notice the traffic light and was nearly knocked down by a car.

(4) These trees were planted one or two years ago, weren't they?

(5) Those old houses have already been torn down.

II. Listening comprehension

Listen to each conversation, then choose an appropriate answer to each question.

(1) A. 邮局　　　　　　B. 银行　　　　　　C. 公司

(2) A. 他不想喝东西　　B. 他不知道喝什么　C. 喝茶或咖啡都可以

(3) A. 能发　　　　　　B. 有时候能发　　　C. 不能发

(4) A. 污染很严重

　　 B. 污染没有以前那么严重

　　 C. 一点儿污染也没有了

(5) A. 他的自行车被人偷走了

　　 B. 警察把自行车还给了他

　　 C. 他在市场上买了一辆新的

(6) A. 男的不是一个好司机

　　 B. 男的不喜欢警察

　　 C. 男的眼睛不好

(7) A. 机场　　　　　　B. 车站　　　　　　C. 路上

III. Oral practice

Question and answer drill with your classmates.

(1) 你的运气怎么样？为什么这么说？

(2) 你觉得现在有哪些污染？我们应该为保护环境做些什么？

IV. Reading comprehension

Read the passage and answer the questions that follow.

　　杰克这次来，发现这儿有了很大的变化。上次来的时候，污染很严重，河水发臭，河里的鱼被毒死了，空气也不好，绿地很少，路两边的树被砍倒了。这次来，河水变清了，河里又有鱼了，天比以前蓝了，地比以前绿了。另外，他还发现，马路比以前干净了，交通也比以前方便了，商店里更热闹了，服务员更客气了。人们穿得比以前更漂亮了。这些都让他觉得高兴。不过，他也看到，高楼造得越来越多了，汽车开得越来越慢了，孩子变得越来越胖了。这些不能不让他有点儿担心。

Answer these questions.

(1) 这个城市的环境有什么变化？

(2) 杰克为什么觉得高兴？

(3) 杰克为什么有点儿担心？

V. Composition

Write a short paragraph about the luckiest event, or the worst situation, that you have ever experienced.

当代中文

Supplementary words

收	(V.)	shōu	to receive
人民币		Rénmínbì	Renminbi
人民	(N.)	rénmín	people
臭	(Adj.)	chòu	smelly, foul
蓝	(Adj.)	lán	blue
绿	(Adj.)	lǜ	green
另外	(Pron., Adv.)	lìngwài	what's more; as well
服务员	(N.)	fúwùyuán	waiter
造	(V.)	zào	to build
胖	(Adj.)	pàng	fat, chubby, plump

Liànxí Cānkǎo Dá'àn
练习参考答案
Key to Exercises

第一课

Ⅱ2 (1)是 (2)姓 (3)叫 (4)说 (5)也 都

(6)也 都 (7)吗 呢

Ⅱ3 (1) 他不是汉语老师。

(2) 他不说英语。

(3) 他们都不是加拿大人。

Ⅱ4 (1) 我是美国人。

(2) 她也是美国人。

(3) 他不是美国人。

(4) 你叫什么名字?

Ⅱ5 (1) 他是你同学吗? /他是不是你同学?

(2) 他说汉语吗? / 他说不说汉语?

(3) 他是张老师吗? /他是不是张老师?

Ⅱ6 (1) 我只说汉语。

(2) 你叫什么名字?

(3) 你是中国人吗? /你是不是中国人?

(4) 你说英语还是法语?

(5) 我不姓王,我姓张。

第二课

Ⅱ2 (1)打 (2)发 (3)认识 (4)工作 (5)喝

Ⅱ3 (1) 我在进出口公司工作。

(2) 他是我们的老师。

(3) 我是东亚学系的学生。

(4) 我可以给你打电话吗? /我可以打电话给你吗?

Ⅱ6 (1) 很高兴认识你! /认识你(我)很高兴!

(2) 请进!

(1) 我在林肯大学东亚(学)系学习。

(2) 他(的)女朋友很漂亮。

(3) 他们(的)大学很大,也很漂亮。

Ⅳ3 请进! 请坐! 请喝茶!

第三课

Ⅱ2 (1)个 (2)口/个 (3)岁 (4)几

(5)多少 (6)两 (7)二

Ⅱ3 (1) 你家有几口人?

(2) 你有几个中国朋友?

(3) 你们学校有多少学生?

(4) 我想去中国工作。

(5) 老板让我去中国工作。

Ⅱ5 (1) 他有两个中国朋友。

(2) 他有很多中国朋友。/他中国朋友很多。

(3) 他没有中国朋友。

(4) 他们学校没有汉语老师。

(5) 我们学校有很多汉语学生。

(6) 你们学校有没有学生学习汉语? /你们学校有学生学习汉语吗?

第四课

Ⅱ2 (1)玩儿 (2)知道 (3)问 (4)用 (5)下

(6)本 (7)个 (8)张 (9)本 (10)支

Ⅱ3 (参考答案)

(1) 那个地方很大，也很漂亮。/不大，也不漂亮。

(2) 他英语好，法语不好。

(3) 他们学校老师比较少，学生非常多。

Ⅱ4 (1) 我喜欢这个，不喜欢那个。

(2) 这张中国地图很有用。

(3) 这本词典很好。

(4) 我能不能用一下你的词典？

(5) 这两本词典是谁的？

第五课

Ⅱ2 (1)和　(2)也　(3)还

Ⅱ3 (1)好吃　(2)大　(3)贵　(4)有意思

(5)红　(6)辣　酸

Ⅱ4 (1)我会说一点儿汉语。

(2)我能不能试一试？/我可不可以试一试？

(3) 先生，您要什么？

(4) 这个菜很好吃。

(5) 我喜欢在小商店买东西。/我喜欢去小商店买东西。

(6) 那儿/那里有一个非常大的商店。

第六课

Ⅱ2 (1) 你下午有空儿吗？/下午你有空儿吗？

(2) 我明天晚上去看你。/明天晚上我去看你。

(3) 我明天在家里休息。/明天我在家里休息。

(4) 我们晚上九点在咖啡馆见面。/晚上九点我们在咖啡馆见面。

(5) 我想请他去打球。

Ⅱ3 (1)打　(2)休息　(3)看　(4)做　(5)喝

Ⅱ5 (1) 你明天上午(打算)干/做什么？

(2) 我今天很忙。

(3) 我明天下午两点半在家里等你。

(4) 他请我今天晚上跟他一起吃饭。/今天晚上他请我跟他一起吃饭。

第七课

Ⅱ2 (1)穿　(2)穿　(3)戴　(4)还是　(5)或者

(6)回　(7)回去　(8)回来　(9)一点儿

(10)一点儿　(11)有点儿　(12)有点儿

(13)不　(14)别

Ⅱ3 (1)高高的　长长的　(2)酸酸的　辣辣的

Ⅱ4 (1)你进来！　(2)你上来！　(3)你过来！

Ⅱ5 (1) 我过一会儿再来。

(2) 他刚出去。

(3) 我下个月四号以前回来。

(4) 那儿的老师都是女的。

第八课

Ⅱ2 (1)怎么　(2)怎么　(3)怎么样　(4)什么

(5)什么　(6)怎么样　(7)怎么　(8)离

(9)从　(10)从　(11)离　(12)有　(13)有

(14)在　(15)在　(16)有

Ⅱ3 马力在上面，江山在下面。

江山在前面，马力在后面。

学生在教室里面，老师在教室外面。

Ⅱ4 王英家左面有一个银行，后面有一个学校，右面有一个商店，前面有一个邮局。

Ⅱ5 (1) 附近有邮局吗？

(1) 我家前面有一个书店。

(2) 地铁站离汽车站不远。

(3) 往前走，往右拐，过一条马路，有一个银行。

(4) 我骑自行车去。

第九课

I 3. (1)办 (2)拍 (3)登 (4)熟悉

(5)张 (6)件 (7)个 (8)只

I 4 (1) 没在那儿吃过 (2)没学过

(3) 没给我打过电话 没给我发过电子邮件

I 5 (1) 会(说汉语)了

(2) 贵了

(3) 不爱(她)了

(4) 有(地铁)了

I 6 (1) 我现在不喜欢了。

(2) 我(以前)没去过那儿。/那儿我(以前)没去过。

(3) 听说他下个月要去北京(了)。

(4) 要是我有时间(的话)，我(就)跟你一起去。

(5) 有的(人)喜欢养狗，有的喜欢养鸟，有的喜欢养鱼。

II (1) A (2) C (3) A (4) C (5) B

(6) A (7) C (8) B

第十课

I 3 (1)干净 (2)着急 (3)疼 (4)舒服

(5)新鲜

I 4 (1) 他肯定已经起床了。

(2) 我还没说完。

(3) 你是不是在进出口公司工作?

(4) 他每天在学校旁边的饭店吃晚饭。

(5) 我昨天给我朋友打了一个电话。/昨天

我给我朋友打了一个电话。

I 5 (1) 他(现在)正在吃早饭。

(2) 昨天我买了一件红衬衫。/我昨天买了一件红衬衫。

(3) 公共汽车还没来。

(4) 我每天六点钟起床。

(5) 她有点儿不舒服。

II (1) A (2) C (3) C (4) B (5) B (6) A

(7) C

第十一课

I 3 (1)不错 (2)先 (3)拿 (4)会

(5)恐怕 (6)应该

I 4 (1) 了 的 的

(2) 了 了 的 的

I 5 (1) 他去过的地方很多。

(2) 他在北京拍的照片很有意思。

(3) 你吃的东西是不是不干净?

(4) 昨天我们去的地方很远。

I 6 (参考答案)

(1) 这是一张照片。

这是我的一张照片。

这是我拍的一张照片。

这是我在北京的时候拍的一张照片。

(2) 我朋友明天要来看我。

我的一位老朋友明天要来看我。

我的一位在北京工作的老朋友明天要来看我。

我的一位在北京工作的姓张的老朋友明天要来看我。

I 7 (1) 你什么时候来的?

(2) 你以前没来过中国，对吗？

是的，我没来过。

(3) 这些都是我在中国拍的照片。

(4) 他对中国文化非常感兴趣。

(5) 能把你昨天买的那张新地图借给我吗？

II (1) A　　(2) A　　(3) C　　(4) B　　(5) C

(6) B　　(7) A　　(8) A

第十二课

I 3 (1)见　(2)送　(3)祝　(4)属　(5)回答

(6)得　(7)的　(8)得　(9)的

I 4 (1) 他们玩得很高兴。

(2) 我每天都睡得比较晚。

(3) 生意越好，老板就越高兴。

(4) 工作做得越多，钱就拿得越多。

I 5 (1) 今天你穿得真漂亮。

(2) 她唱歌唱得很好听。/ 她唱得很好。

(3) 现在东西越来越贵了。

(4) 祝你生日快乐！

(5) 这是我给你的一件小礼物。

II (1) B　(2) B　(3) C　(4) C　(5) B　(6) A

(7) B

第十三课

I 3 (1)滑　(2)下　(3)刮　(4)来　(5)大概

(6)左右

I 4 (1) 今天比昨天热一点儿。/昨天比今天凉快一点儿。

(2) 我们班学生比你们班多。/你们班学生比我们班少。

(3) 小张比小王大两岁。/小王比小张小

两岁。

小张比小王高三厘米。/小王比小张矮三厘米。

小张比小王胖得多。/小王比小张瘦得多。

I 5 (1) 今天很热。

(2) 他没有你高。

(3) 我家乡的夏天比这儿凉快得多。

(4) 这件衣服跟那件一样大。

(5) 你最喜欢哪(一)个季节？

II (1) C　(2) C　(3) C　(4) B　(5) C　(6) C

(7) C

第十四课

I 3 (1)新鲜　优美　(2)方便　(3)热闹　(4)离

(5)从　　　　(6)到　　(7)给　　(8)对

(9)往

I 4 (1) 小楼后面是一个车库。

(2) 我家在美国西部。

(3) 院子里有很多树和花儿。

(4) 他现在可能还在睡觉。/现在他可能还在睡觉。

(5) 他对我们很客气。/我们对他很客气。

I 5 (1) 我家北面是/有一个山，南面是/有一条河。

(2) 你家离海远吗？

(3) 我家东面和西面有很多商店，还有很多饭店。

(4) 我每天开车去学校，大概需要半个小时。

(5) 这件礼物是为你买的。

Ⅱ (1) C　(2) A　(3) C　(4) C　(5) A　(6) B

　　(7) B

第十五课

Ⅰ 3 一年　　　三天

　　一个月　　两个星期

　　一年半　　半天

　　两个半月　半个星期

　　半(个)小时　　25分钟

Ⅰ 4 (1) B　(2) B　(3) B　(4) B　(5) B

Ⅰ 5 (1) 你学了多长时间(的)汉语了?

　　(2) 你能不能再说一遍?

　　(3) 昨天的考试不难。

　　(4) 请你说得慢一点儿。

　　(5) 那儿我去过很多次。/ 我去过那儿很

　　多次。

Ⅱ (1) C　(2) A　(3) C　(4) B　(5) C　(6) A

　　(7) B

第十六课

Ⅰ 3 (1) 参加　(2) 参观　(3) 发生　(4) 打算

　　(5) 安排　(6) 打算　(7) 倒　(8) 破　(9) 坏

　　(10) 伤　(11) 疼

Ⅰ 4 (1) 谈到　(2) 买到　(3) 写错　(4) 打错

　　(5) 吃坏　(6) 摔倒

Ⅰ 5 (1) 戴着　穿着　拿着

　　(2) 坐着

　　(3) 开着

Ⅰ 6 (1) 星期二的火车票都卖完了。

　　(2) 买到票以后请给我们发一个传真, 告诉

　　我们你的航班。

　　(3) 你骑车的时候没看见他在过马路吗?

　　(4) 他骑得很快, 右手还拿着东西。

　　(5) 我们什么时候能学完这本课本?

Ⅱ (1) C　(2) A　(3) B　(4) A　(5) B　(6) B

　　(7) C

第十七课

Ⅰ 3 (1) 锻炼　(2) 练习　(3) 租　(4) 租

　　(5) 发　(6) 送

Ⅰ 4 (1) 出……去　(2) 来　(3) 去　(4) 出来

　　(5) 上……去

Ⅰ 5 (参考答案)

　　(1) 我一有空就出去打工。

　　(2) 我一上完课就回家。

　　(3) 他一回来就看电视。

　　(4) 他一回来, 我就告诉他。

　　(5) 一放假, 我们就去旅行。

Ⅰ 6 (1) 要是你想租的话, 现在就可以搬进去。

　　(2) 每天上楼下楼, 太累了!

　　(3) 这个合同我们可以带回去看一看吗?

　　(4) 我一买到票就给你发传真。

　　(5) 师傅说空调太旧了, 不能修了。

Ⅱ (1) C　(2) C　(3) C　(4) C　(5) A　(6) A

　　(7) B

第十八课

Ⅰ 3 (1) 注意　(2) 教　教　(3) 赶　(4) 爬　爬

　　(5) 跑　(6) 的　(7) 的　(8) 得

　　(9) 地　(10) 得

Ⅰ 4 (1) B　(2) B　(3) C　(4) A

Ⅰ 5 (1) 你可能听不懂, 但是你一定看得懂。

　　(2) 看来我爬不到山顶了。

　　(3) 报纸上说他们都很有名。

(4) 你不是没有时间锻炼，恐怕是太懒了吧。

(5) 这个问题太容易了。连孩子也能回答。

Ⅱ (1) B　(2) A　(3) B　(4) A　(5) A　(6) B
(7) A

第十九课

Ⅰ3 (1)记得　(2)记　(3)记住　(4)刚才
(5)刚　(6)刚才　(7)顿　(8)本
(9)张　(10)遍

Ⅰ4 (参考答案)
(1) ……送给女朋友
(2) 放在楼下
(3) 放在卫生间
(4) 停到车库里去

Ⅰ5 (1) 我把钱包放在座位上了。
(2) 我把钱包忘在车上了。

(3) 他把房间租给了一个外国人。

(4) 咱们把洗衣机搬到卫生间去吧。

(5) 刚才我们下车的时候，是我付的钱。

Ⅱ (1) A　(2) A　(3) B　(4) C　(5) C　(6) B
(7) A

第二十课

Ⅰ3 (1)换　(2)变　(3)寄　(4)打　(5)发

Ⅰ4 (1) B　(2) A　(3) A　(4) A

Ⅰ5 (1) 自行车被人偷走了。

(2) 电脑坏了。

(3) 我骑得太快，没注意红绿灯，差点儿被车撞了一下。

(4) 这些树是一两年前栽的，对吗?

(5) 那些旧房子早就(被)拆掉了。

Ⅱ (1) A　(2) C　(3) C　(4) B　(5) B　(6) A
(7) B

责任编辑：杨 晗
英文编辑：韩芙芸
封面设计：思创文化
插　　图：笑　龙
印刷监制：佟汉冬

图书在版编目（CIP）数据

《当代中文》练习册：英语版 / 吴中伟主编. – 北京：华语教学出版社, 2009

ISBN 978-7-80200-691-1

I. 当… II. 吴… III. 汉语 – 对外汉语教学 – 习题　　IV. H195.4

中国版本图书馆 CIP 数据核字(2009)第200680号

国家汉办网址：www.hanban.org

《当代中文》
练习册
主编　吴中伟
*
©孔子学院总部/国家汉办
华语教学出版社有限责任公司出版
（中国北京百万庄大街24号　邮政编码 100037）
电话：（86）10-68320585 68997826
传真：（86）10-68997826 68326333
网址：www.sinolingua.com.cn
电子信箱：hyjx@sinolingua.com.cn
新浪微博：http://weibo.com/sinolinguavip
北京京华虎彩印刷有限公司印刷
2010年（16开）第1版
2014年第1版第4次印刷
（英语版）
ISBN 978-7-80200-691-1
定价：59.00元